GEOMETRY IN A MODERN SETTING

GUSTAVE CHOQUET

Professor at the Faculty of Sciences, Paris

Geometry
in
a Modern Setting

HERMANN

Publishers in Arts and Science, Paris, France

HOUGHTON MIFFLIN COMPANY · BOSTON

New York · Atlanta · Geneva, Illinois · Dallas · Palo Alto

Translated from the original French text *L'enseignement de la géométrie*,
first published by Hermann in 1964.

Printed in Great Britain

Foreword

This book is written for teachers of mathematics at secondary levels, for people training to be such teachers, and for those who profess a love of geometry. It can also be profitably used by pupils between 15 and 18 years of age under the direction of their teachers.

Euclid based his plane geometry on congruence of triangles. Twenty-three centuries later, mathematicians define a plane as a two-dimensional inner product affine space. It seems to me that children would still benefit from an approach to geometry based, like Euclid's, on concepts drawn from the physical world. But, at the same time, we must do this in such a way that the powerful and flexible tools of algebra are rapidly at our disposal.

Thus, in this book, an axiomatization will be found which bases geometry on the concepts of parallelism, perpendicularity and distance in a manner that rapidly, naturally and easily brings out the algebraic structure of the plane and space.

Finally, several of the later chapters are devoted to clearing up what are traditionally regarded as "thorny" questions, such as deformations, angles, measurement of angles and orientation.

I would like to acknowledge my indebtedness to the many mathematicians and teachers whose discussions have helped so much. In particular, I thank M. André Revuz, whose criticisms and suggestions proved so useful.

GUSTAVE CHOQUET

Contents

1*

§ 4. (Π, 0) *as a vector space*

§ 5. *Dilations of the plane*

§ 6. *Further results*

CHAPTER III. Axioms for metric structure

§ 1. *Perpendiculars*

§ 2. *Inner product*

§ 3. *Elementary metric properties*

CHAPTER IV. Isometries. Similarity transformations. Symmetries of a set

§ 1. *Isometries*

§ 2. *Similitudes*

§ 3. *Sets stable under a group of transformations*

CHAPTER V. Angles

§ 1. *The group of angles*

§ 2. *Angles and similitudes*

CHAPTER VI. Orientation

CHAPTER VII. Trigonometry

§ 1. *Elementary trigonometry*

§ 2. *Measuring angles*

CHAPTER VIII. The Circle

Introduction

I shall not discuss here the need for teaching geometry; I shall simply consider the way in which it can be done.

Nowadays, there is almost universal agreement about the following two principles:

(1) Geometry cannot be taught to the younger students as a formal system. At this stage, it should have a practical basis, and the aim should be to start with everyday experiences and develop the fundamental concepts.

(2) From the mathematician's point of view, the most elegant, mature and incisive method of defining a plane (or space) is as a two- (or three-) dimensional vector space over R having an inner product, i.e. a symmetric bilinear form $u.v$ such that $u.u > 0$ for all non-zero vectors u. This is also the best definition for leading on to important generalizations such as the spaces R^n, C^n, Hilbert space, etc.

Many teachers at the secondary level of education claim that it is their experience that this definition can be profitably used with their 17-year-old pupils (last year of secondary education). Not only does it allow a considerable economy in effort leading naturally to rigorous proofs but, at the same time, it provides valuable assistance to the physics teacher because it finally allows him to define properly things like work, barycentre, resultant of a system of forces.

The problem is less straightforward at the intermediate level, say between 13 and 16 years of age. The pupil has begun to have some idea of what a proof entails, and in some cases a veritable thirst for logic is manifested, suggesting that this is the time for a serious attempt at tackling the problem of formal reasoning. We make the child set out bits of formal reasoning, impressing on him the paramount importance of always stating his premises clearly.

It is, therefore, extremely important that the teacher has at his command an axiomatization which is potentially complete. Besides, various experiments have shown that some children really have a flair for formal axiom systems; they see mathematics as a game to be played in accordance with strict rules, and revel in playing it properly. We need to find a *simple* axiomatization with *strong* and *intuitive* axioms: strong, in the sense that they lead quickly to non-trivial theorems; intuitive, in the sense that they are translations of easily verifiable properties of the space around us.

It does not matter if they are not independent; but starting off with a large number

of axioms, as some teachers advocate, has dubious advantages. If we have too many rules for the game of mathematics, it becomes complex and takes on a rather delicate, uncertain air.

It is well known that Euclid's axiomatization no longer meets the required standards of logic. Although notable efforts can be found in text books published in recent years, the same can also be said of the "axiomatizations" found in the teaching manuals.

Hilbert trimmed and completed Euclid's axiomatization, turning it into a logically satisfactory system; but he was not predominantly concerned with teaching. Nor are the subsequently developed elementary formulations of his axiomatization well suited to classroom needs (see for example that given in Halsted's *Géometrie rationelle*).

The Euclid-Hilbert axiomatization is based on the notions of length, angle and triangle. So marvellously does this conceal the underlying vector space, that the concept of vector remained unrecognized for ages. For over twenty centuries, the fact that a triangle is half of a parallelogram did not prevent mathematicians from placing the accent on detailed studies of heights, medians, perpendicular bisectors and bisections of angles, congruence of triangles, and metric formulas holding in triangles. The triangle was seen, but not the parallelogram which would have led to vectors.

Of course, the triangle will always be of interest to us, if only because it is the simplest plane polygon, and because any triangle determines a unique plane. However, we must vigorously back-pedal on this perverse addiction to those three remarkable points of a triangle, and those occasionally elegant but useless metric formulas that we sometimes find.

Our preference should lie with methods based on those fundamental concepts that two thousand years of mathematics have finally unearthed: set, equivalence relations and orderings, laws of algebra, vector space, symmetry, transformations. Not only do these rapidly enable us to use the powerful, simple tools of algebra, with corresponding economy of effort, but also, because they are rooted in fundamental concepts, they enrich the quality of mind of the pupils and prepare them for the tasks ahead.

A guiding principle for a good axiomatization

How are we to construct an axiomatization which meets our requirements? Ideally, it should enable us to get at the underlying vector space and the properties of the inner product with the minimum of effort.

The situation can be summed up as follows: we have a "royal" road based on the concepts of "vector space and inner product"; but pupils cannot be cannon-balled along this road without preparation, especially at an age when they are not very familiar with algebraic operations.

Even so, it can serve as a guiding principle. We need to take the logically perfect skeleton, which is too abstract for the child, and garb it *discreetly* to take on a recognizable and welcome appearance.

Let us briefly review the basic ideas involved:

(a) That of vector space essentially entails addition on a line and the addition of vectors; the latter can be reduced to parallelism or to the concept of the mid-point of a pair of points.

(b) An inner product is a symmetric bilinear function; we see the part played by addition, and then we meet a new concept, namely symmetry, which cannot be avoided.

(c) An inner product is positive, in the sense that $u.u > 0$ for every $u \neq 0$.

In this way, we find ourselves basing our axiomatization on the *additive structure* of the line, *parallels* and *symmetry*.

Now all text books use symmetry—they cannot avoid it—but very few introduce it in their axioms. For this reason, the axiomatization explicitly given is insufficient and fails to take account of a powerful tool.

Many teachers think symmetry a delicate matter and systematically teach their pupils to use congruence of triangles even in those cases where an obvious symmetry would yield an immediate answer. We must fiercely campaign against this mistrust, and recognize the importance of symmetry right from the very start.

We still have the task of translating the *positiveness* of the inner product into our axiom system. This assumes that the scalar field is ordered, a fact that is translated into an axiom about the ordering of lines. Furthermore, it allows us to define a norm on the space and, from this, a distance which satisfies the triangular inequality. Thus, if the other axioms are not strong enough to derive it, we shall need to add the triangular inequality.

In this book, I present an axiomatization built on these principles.

The metric ideas are completely separated from the affine ideas, and the earlier axioms are sufficient for a complete study of the vectorial structure of the plane or space.[1]

The axioms of incidence I and the axioms of order II would appear to be needed in any sensible axiomatization of the plane. I draw attention to the axiom of incidence I_b, which asserts that there is one and only one line through a given point parallel to a given line. The uniqueness is the feature of Euclid's postulate, the existence coming from the other axioms. My feeling is that by unifying both in the same axiom, we gain considerably in the simplification of the development. Besides, very few pupils under 16 appreciate a proof of existence when to them this existence appears no less empirical than the uniqueness.

In the first instance, I shall develop the axiomatization of the plane; a few additional axioms will then quickly and simply give us the affine and metric structure of space.

For the plane, the axiomatization takes the following pattern. The plane is a set in which the lines are certain subsets. Each line has an algebraic structure and an ordering, these being linked by compatibility axioms, and the structures of the various lines are linked by further appropriate axioms.

In contrast, the axioms of incidence I do not themselves assume any structure on the lines, being entirely concerned with limitations on the abundance of lines and parallels. We shall see that many properties, traditionally regarded as part of the affine or metric structure of the plane, follow, in reality, from Axioms I and II alone.

The role of numbers in geometry

For a long time, the Greeks were only aware of rational numbers and, even after their momentous discovery of the irrational nature of $\sqrt{2}$, they failed to isolate the general

---

1 This was first presented in an O.E.C.E. seminar at Royaumont, in 1959. In an appendix, a second axiomatization is outlined in which the emphasis is placed on the metric properties of the plane and on axial symmetries.

concept of number; for them, this was always linked to geometry. Euclid's successors tried to perfect his work by refining a form of calculus with segments, and although they were able to rediscover by these means that the set of numbers that can be constructed out of plane geometry is a field, it was not done without considerable effort. At all costs, we must avoid this mistake. As soon as possible, the child must think of the set R of numbers as a totally ordered, commutative field: he must realize that when he is carrying out calculations, he is only using a small number of the properties of addition and of multiplication, the ones which mathematicians call the axioms for totally ordered commutative fields.

Later on, depending on his needs, he will use Archimedes' axiom (possibly in the form: Every number is less than some integer) or the stronger axiom of continuity (for example: Every subset of R bounded above has a least upper bound).

No doubt, when teaching, the algebraic properties of various operations can be conveniently illustrated by reference to the line; but this is not plane geometry. Any resort in plane geometry to a calculus of segments involving ideas already borrowed from plane geometry, such as parallels, transversals, or even perpendiculars, must be strictly avoided.

Axioms of incidence and order

1. Lines and parallels

1. DEFINITIONS

A plane consists of a set Π and a family $\mathscr{D}$ of subsets of Π which are called lines. Each line has a structure satisfying certain axioms, and the structures of the various lines are interrelated by further axioms called linking axioms.

At the very outset, we postulate the following.

Axiom 0. The plane contains at least two lines, and every line contains at least two points.

This is numbered 0 because it will be a redundant axiom. Axiom III_a will guarantee the existence of two or more points on a line, while Axiom IV_a will imply that the plane contains at least two lines. Even so, it is as well to include it because it simplifies the exposition in the earlier stages.

Before introducing the other Axioms, we require some definitions.

Definition 1.1. Two lines A, B of Π *are said to be parallel (written* A ∥ B) *if either* A = B, *or* A ∩ B = ∅.

In several texts, parallelism is defined by the weaker condition A ∩ B = ∅. This is not a very happy choice of definition because it obscures the rather useful equivalence relation which we shall soon obtain. Let us simply note, in passing, that by definition, parallelism is a reflexive and symmetric relation on $\mathscr{D}$.

The following terminology is useful.

A line A is a *transversal* of (or *cuts*) a line B if their intersection consists of a single point.

A line D *passes* through a if $a \in$ D.

A subset X of Π is *collinear* if there is some line containing it.

2. AXIOMS OF INCIDENCE

Axiom I_a. For every pair (x, y) of distinct points of Π, there is one and only one line containing x and y.

Axiom I_b. If D is a line, and x is a point, there is one and only one line parallel to D passing through x.

The line passing through a pair (x, y) of distinct points of Π is denoted by $\Delta(x, y)$.

By Axiom I_a, saying that two lines cut is the same as saying that they are not parallel.

Proposition 2.1. Parallelism is an equivalence relation on $\mathcal{D}$.

We already know that parallelism is reflexive and symmetric and need only show that it is transitive.

Suppose A ∥ B and B ∥ C.

If $A \cap C = \varnothing$, the result is proved. If not, A and C are both parallel to B and have a point in common. By I_b, A = C, and this proves the result.

With any equivalence relation **R** on a set E, we can associate a partitioning of E into classes, which can be regarded as the elements of a new set written E/**R**. In the light of this remark, we make the following definition.

Definition 2.2. The equivalence classes in $\mathcal{D}$ associated with parallelism are called directions. The direction *of a line is the equivalence class that it belongs to.*

The fact that two lines are parallel, can now be expressed by saying that their directions are the same. Also, through any point, there is one and only one line with a given direction.

In concrete situations, it is often useful to specify a direction δ by picking out one of the lines with that direction.

Proposition 2.3. If D is a line, the complement of D is non-empty.

Proof. Let D′ be a line other than D.

If D′ ∥ D, the complement of D contains D′.

If D′ and D cut, take a as their point of intersection. By Axiom 0, there is an $x \in D′$ such that $x \neq a$ and, furthermore, $x \notin D$.

Hence, in both cases, there is a point not on D, and this proves the result.

Proposition 2.4. Let D be a line, and let a be a point such that $a \notin D$. ($\Delta(a, x)$ is thus defined for all $x \in D$).

The map $x \to \Delta(a, x)$ from D into $\mathcal{D}$ is a bijection of D onto the set of lines passing through a but not parallel to D.

Proof. The map is injective because any line through a meets D in at most one point.

It is surjective because no line $\Delta(a, x)$ is parallel to D, and every line cutting D meets D in a unique point x and is then $\Delta(a, x)$ for this x.

Corollary 2.5. There are at least three directions.

For (in the notation of 2.4) D contains at least two points, and consequently there are at least three lines through a; namely, the parallel to D and the lines $\Delta(a, x)$, where $x \in D$.

*Proposition 2.6. Let δ be a direction, and let **R** be the binary relation on Π given by:*

$$(x \sim y) \quad \text{if there is some line with direction δ containing } x \text{ and } y.$$

Then **R** *is an equivalence relation on* Π *and the classes are the lines whose direction is* δ.

Proof. The lines with direction δ partition Π because they certainly cover Π and they are either equal or disjoint.

Also, if *x* is a point, the set of points *y* such that *x* ∼ *y* is precisely that line through *x* with direction δ. The relation **R** is therefore the equivalence relation associated with this partitioning.

Remark. It is important to distinguish carefully between this relation **R** and the relation of parallelism. The former is an equivalence relation on Π (and also depends on δ), while the latter is on 𝒟.

3. Oblique projection

If D is a line, and δ a direction other than that of D (such a direction exists by 2.5), then, for every point *m* ∈ Π, the line through *m* whose direction is δ meets D in a unique point φ(*m*).

Definition 3.1. The mapping φ *from* Π *into* D *is called the* oblique projection *on* D *parallel to* δ. *When* δ *is the direction of some line* A, *we also speak of the projection as being parallel to* A.

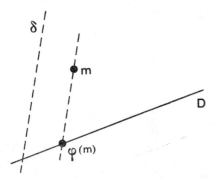

Clearly, the fixed points of φ, i.e. the points *x* satisfying φ(*x*) = *x*, are just those points of D. Moreover

$$\varphi(\Pi) = D \quad \text{and} \quad \varphi(D) = D$$

The oblique projection is one of the basic tools of geometry. As we adjoin the further axioms, its usefulness will become more and more apparent.

Often it will be convenient to call the restriction of an oblique projection to a subset of Π an oblique projection as well.

Proposition 3.2. Let A, B *be a pair of lines and* δ *be a direction other than those of* A, B (δ *exists by 2.5). Then the oblique projection of* A *into* B *parallel to* δ *is a bijection.*

Proof. Let φ be the parallel projection. It is an injection because whenever *x*, *x'* are distinct points of A, the lines through them with direction δ are also distinct, and therefore

meet B in distinct points. It is a surjection because, if y is a point of B, the line with direction δ passing through y meets A in that point x satisfying $\varphi(x) = y$.

Obviously, the oblique projection of B onto A parallel to δ is simply φ^{-1}.

Corollary 3.3. All lines in Π *have the same cardinal.* (*This cardinal will be denoted by* α; *it can be infinite or finite depending on the particular plane* Π *that we are interested in.*)

Remark. The symmetry in the roles played by A, B in the projections φ, φ^{-1} is well illustrated by the following.

The partitioning of Π by lines with direction δ induces a partitioning of $A \cup B$ in which every class contains two points x and $\varphi(x)$, one from A, the other from B. These points are distinct unless A and B cut, in which case, $x = \varphi(x)$ when $\{x\} = A \cap B$.

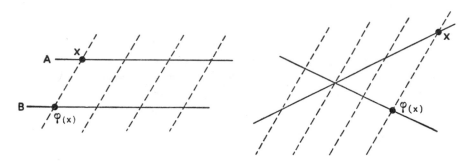

4. Systems of axes

Let D_1, D_2 be a pair of intersecting lines. Write φ_1 for the oblique projection on D_1 parallel to D_2, and φ_2 for that on D_2 parallel to D_1.

For $m \in \Pi$, the points $\varphi_1(m)$, $\varphi_2(m)$ are called the *components of* m relative to the system of axes (D_1, D_2). The intersection of D_1 and D_2 is called the *origin* of the system.

To each pair (m_1, m_2) of points of Π such that $m_1 \in D_1$ and $m_2 \in D_2$, there corresponds exactly one point m which has m_1, m_2 as its components. This point is the intersection of the line through m_1 parallel to D_2 and the line through m_2 parallel to D_1.

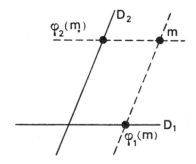

The map $m \to (\varphi_1(m), \varphi_2(m))$ is therefore a bijection of Π *onto* the product set $D_1 \times D_2$.

This is really what we mean when we say that (D_1, D_2) is a reference frame for the plane and that every point of Π is determined by its two components. It follows in particular that Π has cardinal α^2.

3. Axioms of order

The first axiom introduces an ordering on each line. The second links the various orderings.

5. THE ORDERING OF A LINE

Axiom II_a. Every line has two total orderings, the one the reverse of the other.

This is put in a rather condensed form because it presupposes what is meant by a total ordering on a set.

We bring in both total orderings on a line because there is no canonical method of singling one of them out as being natural or special in any sense. Obviously, once one of them is known, so is the other. We could avoid this device of two orderings by using instead a ternary relation such as "x is between y and z" (subject, of course, to suitable axioms). The trouble with a relation of this sort is that it is not as easy to handle as an order relation, simply because it is ternary.

Terminology. 1. An *orientated line* is a pair $(D, \leqslant)$, where D is a line and $\leqslant$ is one of its total orderings. When the particular ordering "$\leqslant$" chosen is not important, we shall simply write "the orientated line D".

2. If a, b is a pair of distinct points the expression "orientated line $\Delta(a, b)$" means the line $\Delta(a, b)$ orientated so that $a \leqslant b$.

3. If D is an orientated line and $a \in D$, the *positive open half-line* whose origin is at a is the set $\{x \mid a < x\}$. The *positive closed half-line* is the set $\{x \mid a \leqslant x\}$. The expression "half-line $D(a, b)$" means the *positive* (open or closed) half-line with origin a in the orientated line $\Delta(a, b)$.

4. If a, b are distinct points of Π, the line $\Delta(a, b)$ is unique and the intervals $[a, b]$, (a, b), $[a, b)$ are the same, whichever total ordering is chosen. Thus these intervals are well defined for any line, orientated or otherwise. Note that $[a, a] = a$ and $(a, a) = \varnothing$.

Definition 5.1. A *non-empty subset* X *of* Π *is said to be* convex *if* $[x, y] \subset X$, *whenever* $x, y \in X$.

For example, Π is convex, so is every half-line and every interval. Soon, we shall give other important examples.

Obviously, the intersection of any family (X_i) of convex sets in Π is also convex. If A is any non-empty subset of Π, there must be convex sets containing A because Π

itself is such a set. It follows then that the intersection of all such sets is convex, and it is the smallest convex set containing A. This set is called the *convex envelope* of A.

6. LINKING AXIOM

Axiom II$_b$. (Linking the orderings on the various lines.)

If A, B are parallel lines and a, a', b, b' points such that a, $a' \in$ A and b, $b' \in$ B, then any line parallel to A and B intersecting $[a, b]$ also intersects $[a', b']$.

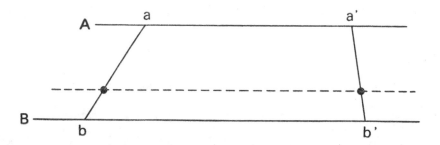

Notice that if A = B, the axiom collapses to an obvious consequence of previous definitions. It is only interesting for A ≠ B.

Proposition 6.1. If D is a line, δ a direction distinct from that of D, and φ the oblique projection on D parallel to δ, then, for all $x, y \in \Pi$,

$$\varphi([x, y]) = [\varphi(x), \varphi(y)]$$

Proof. When x and y lie on a line whose direction is δ, this is obvious because φ is constant for such lines, giving

$$\varphi([x, y]) = \{\varphi(x)\} = \{\varphi(y)\}$$

Otherwise, take A and B as the lines with direction δ through x and y respectively. The proposition is now a consequence of Axiom II$_b$ which effectively states that φ is a bijection from $[x, y]$ onto $[\varphi(x), \varphi(y)]$.

Corollary 6.2. If X *is any convex set, its projection* φ(X) *on* D *is also convex.*
For every convex set X ⊂ D, $\varphi^{-1}(X)$ *is convex.*

Corollary 6.3. If A, B are two orientated lines, and δ is a direction other than those of A or B, then the oblique projection of A onto B parallel to δ is either strictly monotone increasing or strictly monotone decreasing (interpreted in terms of the orders on A and B).

This is really a consequence of 6.2, which implies that if $x, y, z \in$ A with $x \leqslant y \leqslant z$, then $\varphi(x) \leqslant \varphi(y) \leqslant \varphi(z)$. With this property, φ must be either strictly monotone increasing or strictly monotone decreasing.

Corollary 6.4. If the cardinal α of the lines of Π *satisfies* α > 2, *every open half-line of* Π *is nonempty.*

Proof. Let D be any line and take $a \in D$. There exists a line D' which is parallel to D but not equal to D and, by hypothesis, there exist at least three distinct points a', x', y' on D. Evidently, we can assume that $a' \in [x', y']$.

Now the direction of $\Delta(a, a')$ cannot be that of D nor that of D'. Hence (Props. 3.2 and 6.1) the projections a, x, y of a', x', y' on D parallel to $\Delta(a, a')$ are distinct and $a \in [x, y]$.

Thus, the two open half-lines in D originating at a are both non-empty, and it is fairly clear that this also shows that the cardinal α is infinite.

The above result is convenient at this stage, but becomes trivial once we have Axiom III at our disposal.

7. DIVISION OF THE PLANE BY A LINE

Proposition 7.1. Suppose the cardinal α of the lines satisfies $\alpha > 2$. Then, for every line D, there is a unique partitioning of $\Pi - D$ into two convex subsets Π_1, Π_2. Neither of these sets is empty, and, if $x_1 \in \Pi_1, x_2 \in \Pi_2$, the interval $[x_1, x_2]$ always meets D.

Proof. 1. *Existence.* Let A be a transversal of D and let a be their point of intersection. Let φ be the projection on A parallel to D and A_1, A_2 be the open half-lines of A originating at a. These half-lines are convex and partition $A - \{a\}$. By Corollary 6.2, the two subsets $\Pi_i = \varphi^{-1}(A_i)$ $(i = 1, 2)$ are convex, and they partition $\Pi—D$.

2. *Uniqueness.* Let (E_1, E_2) be a second partition satisfying the required properties. Each $\varphi(E_i)$ is convex and is contained in $A_1 \cup A_2$. As the only convex subsets of $A_1 \cup A_2$ are contained either in A_1 or in A_2, each E_i must be contained in one of the Π_i. From $E_1 \cup E_2 = \Pi_1 \cup \Pi_2$, it then follows that either $E_1 = \Pi_1$ and $E_2 = \Pi_2$, or $E_1 = \Pi_2$ and $E_2 = \Pi_1$. However, in both cases, the partition is the same.

3. Suppose $x_1 \in X_1, x_2 \in X_2$. The interval $\varphi[x_1, x_2]$ then has its extremities in A_1 and A_2 respectively, and must therefore contain a. Thus $[x_1, x_2]$ meets $\varphi^{-1}(\{a\}) = D$, and the proof is complete.

Definition 7.2. The sets Π_1, Π_2 defined in Prop. 7.1 are called the open half-planes associated with D.

The sets $\Pi_1 \cup D$ and $\Pi_2 \cup D$ are called the closed half-planes associated with D.

Notice that the closed half-planes are also convex because $\Pi_i \cup D$ is the inverse image of $A_i \cup \{a\}$ under φ.

Exercises on Chapter I

The following exercises are in no way necessary to the subsequent development, and many of them can be solved much more simply at a later stage. They are included to provide practice in manipulating axioms at a time when few theorems are available.

1. Let E be a set and $\mathscr{L}$ a set of subsets of E.

For $L_1, L_2 \in \mathscr{L}$, we shall say that L_1 is parallel to L_2 (written $L_1 \parallel L_2$) if either $L_1 = L_2$ or $L_1 \cap L_2 = \varnothing$.

Assume that $\mathscr{L}$ satisfies the axiom:

"For $L \in \mathscr{L}$ and $a \in E$, there exists a unique $L' \in \mathscr{L}'$ such that $a \in L'$ and $L' \parallel L$."

Show that this axiom is equivalent to the requirement that the parallelism defined is an equivalence relation on $\mathscr{L}$.

Finally an element $L \in \mathscr{L}$ is chosen and a relation on Π defined by the rule

"$(a \sim b)$ if there exists $L' \in \mathscr{L}'$ with $L' \parallel L$ and $a, b \in L'$"

By means of the axiom, show that this is always an equivalence relation, and that the classes are elements of $\mathscr{L}$ parallel to L.

2. Let K be any commutative field, and let any subset of K^2 satisfying a relation of the form

$$a_1 x_1 + a_2 x_2 = b \qquad \text{(where } a_1, a_2, b \in K; a_1 \text{ and } a_2 \text{ not both zero)}$$

be called a line of K^2.

Show that K^2 with these lines satisfies Axiom I.

3. Examine the particular case in which K is finite (e.g. the integers mod p, where p is a prime).

Examine also the case where K is the complex number field.

In the remaining exercises, we assume that *Axioms I and II are satisfied*.

4. Show that, if the cardinal α of the lines is not 2 (in which case Π is isomorphic to K^2, where K is the field of two elements), the cardinal of any open interval (a, b) is infinite whenever $a \neq b$.

More exactly, show that every open half-line and every non-empty open interval is order isomorphic to any given line.

5. Let A, B, C be three half-lines with the same origin 0 such that no two are collinear.

Show that either any two lie one on each side of the line carrying the third, or there is a line not through 0 cutting all three.

6. Let A, B be a pair of non-collinear half-lines with the same origin 0.

Define the *sector* (A, B) to be the intersection of the half-plane associated with B containing A and the half-plane associated with A containing B. Let D be any half-line originating at 0 which is contained in the sector (A, B) but is neither A nor B.

Show that D meets every line segment $[a, b]$ such that $a \in A$ and $b \in B$, and therefore every line parallel to A meeting B.

7. Deduce from the previous exercise, that if (a, b, c) is a non-collinear triplet and c' is the intersection of the lines parallel to $\Delta(a, c)$, $\Delta(b, c)$ through b and a respectively, then c and c' are on opposite sides of $\Delta(a, b)$.

Show that (a, b) meets (c, c').

8. Let 0, a, b be three points of Π not collinear. Let $a' \in [0, a]$, $b' \in [0, b]$. Show that for $m \in [a, b]$, $[0, m]$ and $[a', b']$ must intersect.

Deduce from this that the union of intervals $[0, x]$ joining a point 0 to points x of a convex set, is again convex.

Extend this result to the union of intervals joining the points of two given convex sets.

9. Show that the convex envelope of a finite subset (the smallest convex set containing it) is the intersection of a finite family of closed half-planes.

In particular, show that the convex envelope of a non-collinear triple (a, b, c) is the intersection of the closed half-planes associated with $\Delta(a, b)$, $\Delta(b, c)$, $\Delta(c, a)$ containing c, a, b respectively. Such a set is called a simplex.

10. Give several equivalent definitions of the plane *strip* defined by the two parallel lines A, B. In what follows, the direction of a strip will be the direction of the defining lines.

11. A subset X of Π is said to be *bounded* if it can be encompassed in a plane strip with direction δ, for every direction δ.

Show that any finite set is bounded.

Show that a subset X which is contained in two plane strips with different directions is also bounded.

Show that any bounded set is contained in a simplex.

12. (a) Define a topology on the line starting with the notion of an open interval (refer to any book on topology for the definition of this word).

(b) Let D_1, D_2 be a pair of intersecting lines in Π. By identifying Π with $D_1 \times D_2$ obtain a topology on Π from the product of the topologies on D_1 and D_2. Show that the topology obtained is independent of the choice of D_1, D_2.

13. Let $X \subset \Pi$ and a, $b \in X$. Set $(a \sim b)$ if there exists a polygonal line in X whose end points are a and b. Show that this is an equivalence relation on X. (The equivalence classes are called the components of X.)

Now suppose P is a *closed* polygon without double points, i.e. two sides which are not consecutive do not intersect, and let C be the bounding curve of P (the union of its sides).

Show that $(\Pi - C)$ has precisely two components, one of which is bounded, and that in the topology on Π, each of these components is open. Show also that every point of C is a limit point of both components. (Jordan.)

The solution is elementary but not trivial. The reader is advised to consider a direction δ which is not parallel to any of the sides of the polygon and to draw lines with direction δ through each vertex. The set of such parallels should then be ordered and successive strips examined.

14. Let K be a totally ordered commutative field $((a \leqslant b) \Rightarrow (a + x \leqslant b + x)$ and $(0 \leqslant a, 0 \leqslant b) \Rightarrow (0 \leqslant ab))$. Show that K^2 can be made into a plane which satisfies Axioms I and II (see first Ex. 2). Give examples of such fields K which are not subfields of the real field R.

15. Let Π be an open disc in R^2 in the classical sense. Call any circular arc in Π whose endpoints are the extremities of a diameter of Π a "line", and order this "line" in the natural way.

Show that Π satisfies Axioms I and II but it is not order isomorphic to the plane R^2 even though its "lines" are isomorphic to R.

Construct other similar families in the open disc Π by taking the "lines" as certain families of arcs, invariant under rotations, having extremities which are the extremities of a diameter of the disc. (To investigate whether or not such planes are isomorphic to the classical plane, use a property of networks built up from two sets of parallel lines.)

Axioms for affine structure

I. Affine structure of lines

8. First affine axiom

Although the axiom that we are about to state involves the real numbers, from the point of view of this chapter we need R to be only a totally ordered, Archimedean commutative field. Continuity is not required. For this reason, it is quite possible to teach 12 to 16 year olds without mentioning the completeness of R, or any of the equivalent notions, such as upper bound, cut, monotone sequence, Cauchy sequence.

Axiom III_a. Affine structure of a line.

There exists a mapping d from $\Pi \times \Pi$ into R_+, called *distance*, satisfying the following properties:

1. $d(y, x) = d(x, y)$ for all $x, y \in \Pi$.

2. If D is an orientated line, $x \in D$, and l is a positive number, then there exists a unique point y of D such that

$$x \leqslant y \quad \text{and} \quad d(x, y) = l$$

3. $$(x \in [a, b]) \Rightarrow (d(a, x) + d(x, b) = d(a, b))$$

This is an axiom concerning the affine structure of individual lines. It will be complemented by Axiom III_b which will link the affine structures of the various lines.

Immediate consequences

1. By III_a, $d(x, y) = d(x, x) + d(x, y)$, for all x, y; i.e. $d(x, x) = 0$. If $x \neq y$, but $x < y$, the relation $x \leqslant x \leqslant y$ implies (by III_a) that $d(x, y) \neq 0$. Thus, $(d(x, y) = 0) \Leftrightarrow (x = y)$.

2. Again, by III_a, $(x \in [a, b]) \Rightarrow (d(a, x) \leqslant d(a, b))$, and equality only holds when $x = b$.

9. Isomorphism of R and pointed lines of Π

Proposition 9.1. Let D *be an orientated line and a be a point of* D. *Then there is a unique monotone increasing map f from* D *to* R *such that*

$$f(a) = 0 \quad and \quad d(x, y) = |f(y) - f(x)|, \quad for \; all \; x, y \in D$$

Moreover, f is a bijection from D *to* R.

Proof. 1. *Uniqueness.*

The defining relations of f imply that $d(x, a) = |f(x)|$ (put $y = a$). Because f is monotone increasing, with $f(a) = 0$, it follows that

$$f(x) = d(a, x) \quad \text{if } a < x$$
$$f(x) = -d(a, x) \quad \text{if } x < a$$

2. We show that the map f defined by these last equalities satisfies the conditions of the proposition. By Axiom III_a,

$$(x \leqslant a \leqslant y) \Rightarrow (d(x, y) = d(x, a) + d(a, y) = -f(x) + f(y))$$
$$(a \leqslant x \leqslant y) \Rightarrow (d(a, y) = d(a, x) + d(x, y)) \quad \text{or} \quad f(y) = f(x) + d(x, y)$$
$$(x \leqslant y \leqslant a) \Rightarrow (d(x, a) = d(x, y) + d(y, a)) \quad \text{or} \quad -f(x) = d(x, y) - f(y)$$

Thus, in all cases,

$$(x \leqslant y) \Rightarrow (d(x, y) = f(y) - f(x))$$

However, as $d(x,y) > 0$ for $x \neq y$, this shows that $f(x) < f(y)$, whenever $x < y$, i.e. f is monotone increasing.

As for the bijective properties of f, we can say that f is injective because

$$(x < y) \Rightarrow (f(y) - f(x) = d(x, y) \neq 0)$$

It is surjective because, by III_a, there exist x, y such that

$$a \leqslant x \quad \text{and} \quad d(a, x) = l \quad \text{i.e.} \quad f(x) = l$$
$$y \leqslant a \quad \text{and} \quad d(a, y) = l \quad \text{i.e.} \quad f(x) = -l$$

Consequences. This shows that an orientated pointed line (i.e. a pair (D, 0) where D is a line and 0 an origin on that line) is isomorphic to R under a unique isomorphism preserving distance and order.

From now on, whenever it is convenient, we will be able to identify an orientated pointed line with R, using f to carry over to the orientated line all properties of R. In particular, taking (D, 0) as the pointed line, and f as its canonical map on to R, we have:

1. The *abscissa* of x in (D, 0) is $f(x)$, and its value is $d(0, x)$ or $-d(0, x)$ depending on whether $0 < x$ or $x < 0$.

2. The *algebraic distance* between a pair (x, y) of points of (D, 0) is the number

$$\overline{xy} = f(y) - f(x) = \overline{0y} - \overline{0x}$$

Its value is $d(x, y)$ or $-d(x, y)$ depending on whether $x \leqslant y$ or $y \leqslant x$. Notice that it is

independent of the origin, and changes sign when we reverse the ordering of D. Chasles' relation obviously holds.

Often, when we are keeping the same origin 0 throughout a piece of work it is useful to use the same notation for x and its abscissa. This makes the calculations easier because, for example, $\overline{xy}$ becomes $y - x$, as in R.

3. The orientated pointed line (D, 0) is a vector space of dimension 1 with 0 as null vector.

4. In (D, 0) *translation by a* is the map $x \to x + a$. It is an isometry.

A *dilation* is a transformation of the form $x \to kx + a$ $(k \in R^*)$. This is an isometry only if $k = \pm 1$ (translation or symmetry). Conversely, any isometry of D is a translation or a symmetry.

5. The mid-point of a pair (x, y) of distinct points is the point m of $\Delta(x, y)$ uniquely defined by the equation $m - x = y - m$, obtained by regarding $\Delta(x, y)$ as a pointed line. The point m is independent of the choice of origin on $\Delta(x, y)$, being the point $\frac{1}{2}(x + y)$. The mid-point of (x, x) is x.

6. If $x, y, z \in D$, then

$$d(x, z) \leqslant d(x, y) + d(x, z), \quad \text{equality holding only if } y \in [x, z]$$

7. It is possible to divide (x, y) in any given ratio.

8. Homographies and involutions can be defined on D completed with the point at infinity.

2. Additive group structure of (Π, 0)

10. LINKING AXIOM

Axiom III$_b$. (*Relating the affine structures of the various lines.*)

If A, B are parallel lines and a, b, a', b' points such that $a, a' \in A$ and $b, b' \in B$, then the line parallel to these lines through the mid-point of (a, b) also passes through the mid-point of (a', b').

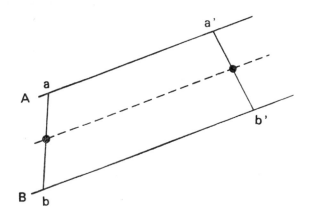

This is the axiom that enables us to define a group structure on Π after choosing an origin.

11. Oblique parallel projections and parallelograms

Lemma 11.1. Let D *be a line,* δ *a direction other than that of* D, *and* φ *the oblique projection on* D *parallel to* δ. *Then,*

$$(m \text{ is mid-point of } (x, y)) \Rightarrow (\varphi(m) \text{ is mid-point of } (\varphi(x), \varphi(y)))$$

We generally express this by saying that oblique projection preserves mid-points.

Proof. Let A, B be the lines through x, y respectively whose direction is δ. By Axiom III$_b$, the line with direction δ passing through m also passes through the mid-point of $(\varphi(x), \varphi(y))$.

Thus, the lemma is really just another form of Axiom III$_b$.

Corollary 11.2. Let (D_1, D_2) *be a system of axes, and* x, y, m *be three points of* Π *with components* $(x_1, x_2), (y_1, y_2), (m_1, m_2)$ *respectively. Then,*

$$(m \text{ is mid-point of } (x, y))$$
$$\Leftrightarrow (m_1 \text{ is mid-point of } (x_1, y_1) \text{ and } m_2 \text{ is mid-point of } (x_2, y_2))$$

Definition 11.3. A parallelogram *is a quadruplet* (a, b, a', b') *of points of* Π *such that* (a, a') *and* (b, b') *have the same mid-point.*

The pairs (a, a') *and* (b, b') *are called its* diagonals.

Clearly, if (a, b, a', b') is a parallelogram so is (a, b', a', b).

If x, y, m are points of Π, we say that x and y are symmetric about m if m is the mid-point of (x, y). When x and m are prescribed, then there is a unique point y which is symmetric to x about m (if $x = m, y = m$; if $x \neq m, y$ is that point of the orientated line $\Delta(x, m)$ given by $\overline{xm} = \overline{my}$).

Definition 11.4. Let $m \in \Pi$. Symmetry with centre m *is the mapping* s *from* Π *into itself which maps each point* x *to the point* $s(x)$ *symmetric to* x *about* m.

Evidently, s^2 is the identity and so s is an involutory transformation of Π.

We can redefine a parallelogram in terms of central symmetries because we have the obvious equivalence:

$$((a, b, a', b') \text{ is a parallelogram})$$
$$\Leftrightarrow (a', b' \text{ are the images of } a, b \text{ under a central symmetry})$$

From this, we see that if three points a, b, b' of Π are prescribed, there is a unique fourth point a' such that (a, b, a', b') is a parallelogram. The point a' is characterized as the point symmetric to a about the mid-point of (b, b').

Corollary 11.5 (to Lemma 11.1). *The image of a parallelogram under an oblique projection is again a parallelogram.*

For, by Lemma 11.1, if (a, a') and (b, b') have the same mid-point, so do $(\varphi(a), \varphi(a'))$ and $(\varphi(b), \varphi(b'))$.

12. Addition in $(\Pi, 0)$ and its group structure

For every point $0 \in \Pi$, the expression "*pointed plane* $(\Pi, 0)$" means the plane Π with an origin chosen at 0.

Definition 12.1. Addition in $(\Pi, 0)$ *is the binary operator on* Π *defined by* $(x, y) \rightarrow x \mathsf{T} y$, *where* $x \mathsf{T} y$ *is the unique point* z *such that* $(0, x, z, y)$ *is a parallelogram.*

Lemma 12.2. If D *is a line through* 0, *then:*

1. *The restriction to* D *of the operation* T *is identical to addition in the pointed line* $(\mathrm{D}, 0)$.

2. *For every oblique projection* φ *on* D,

$$\varphi(x \mathsf{T} y) = \varphi(x) \mathsf{T} \varphi(y) \quad \text{for all } x, y$$

Proof. 1. When $x, y \in \mathrm{D}$, $x \mathsf{T} y$ is that point z of D such that $(0, x, y, z)$ is a parallelogram. This point is $x + y$. It follows that D is closed under T, and is an abelian group.

2. By Corollary 11.5, the projection $(0, \varphi(x), \varphi(x \mathsf{T} y), \varphi(y))$ of the parallelogram $(0, x, x \mathsf{T} y, y)$ is a parallelogram, and this proves the result.

Theorem 12.3. 1. *Under the operator* T, *the pointed plane* $(\Pi, 0)$ *is an abelian group with null element* 0.

2. *Any line through* 0 *is a subgroup.*

3. *If* $\mathrm{D}_1, \mathrm{D}_2$ *is a pair of distinct lines through* 0, *the group* $(\Pi, 0)$ *is the direct sum of the subgroups* D_1 *and* D_2; *i.e. every* $x \in \Pi$ *can be uniquely written as* $x = x_1 \mathsf{T} x_2$, *where* $x_1 \in \mathrm{D}_1$, $x_2 \in \mathrm{D}_2$, x_1, x_2 *being the components of* x *in the system of axes* $(\mathrm{D}_1, \mathrm{D}_2)$.

4. *A translation of* $(\Pi, 0)$ *transforms a line through* 0 *onto a parallel line. Every line is the translate of some line through* 0.

Proof. 1. Let $\mathrm{D}_1, \mathrm{D}_2$ be a pair of distinct lines through 0. Let φ_1, φ_2 denote the projections on $\mathrm{D}_1, \mathrm{D}_2$ parallel to $\mathrm{D}_2, \mathrm{D}_1$ respectively. By Lemma 12.2, for all $x, y, z \in \Pi$,

$$\varphi_i(x \mathsf{T} y) = \varphi_i(x) \mathsf{T} \varphi_i(y) = \varphi_i(y) \mathsf{T} \varphi_i(x) = \varphi_i(y \mathsf{T} x) \quad (i = 1, 2)$$

$$\varphi_i((x \mathsf{T} y) \mathsf{T} z) = (\varphi_i(x) \mathsf{T} \varphi_i(y)) \mathsf{T} \varphi_i(z) = \varphi_i(x) \mathsf{T} (\varphi_i(y) \mathsf{T} \varphi_i(z))$$
$$= \varphi_i(x \mathsf{T} (y \mathsf{T} z)) \quad (i = 1, 2)$$

Hence $x \mathsf{T} y$ and $y \mathsf{T} x$ have the same components in the system of axes $(\mathrm{D}_1, \mathrm{D}_2)$ and they are therefore equal. Similarly,

$$(x \mathsf{T} y) \mathsf{T} z = x \mathsf{T} (y \mathsf{T} z)$$

Thus T is commutative and associative. The element 0 is obviously a null element under T, and inverses exist because for every x, the point x' symmetric to x about 0 clearly satisfies $x \mathsf{T} x' = 0$.

2. This is proved in Lemma 12.2.

3. Take $x \in \Pi$, and let x_1, x_2 be its components in the system $(\mathrm{D}_1, \mathrm{D}_2)$.
   Now $\varphi_1(x_1 \mathsf{T} x_2) = \varphi_1(x_1) \mathsf{T} \varphi_1(x_2) = x_1 \mathsf{T} 0 = x_1$. Similarly, $\varphi_2(x_1 \mathsf{T} x_2) = x_2$. In other words, $x_1 \mathsf{T} x_2$ has x_1, x_2 as components, and so $x_1 \mathsf{T} x_2 = x$.
   Next, suppose $x = y_1 \mathsf{T} y_2$ with $y_1 \in \mathrm{D}_1, y_2 \in \mathrm{D}_2$. Then,

$$x_1 = \varphi_1(x) = \varphi_1(y_1 \mathsf{T} y_2) = y_1 \mathsf{T} 0 = y_1$$

and, similarly, $x_2 = y_2$.

Thus the decomposition is unique and is of the required form.

4. Let D_1 be a line passing through 0, and let $a \in \Pi$.

If $a \in D_1$, $(D_1 \, T \, a) = D_1$ because D_1 is a subgroup.

If $a \notin D_1$, the line D_2 containing both 0 and a is not D_1 and so the pair (D_1, D_2) is a system of axes whose origin is 0. Letting D_1' be the line parallel to D_1 passing through a, it follows that

$$(x \in D_1') \Leftrightarrow (x_2 = a) \Leftrightarrow (x = a \, T \, x_1, \text{ where } x_1 \in D_1) \Leftrightarrow (x \in a \, T \, D_1)$$

Thus $D_1' = a \, T \, D_1$, as required.

It is now also clear that if D_1' is a line not through 0, it must be a translate of the line D_1 parallel to D_1' which does pass through 0. In fact, for any $a \in D_1'$, $D_1' = a \, T \, D_1$.

Notation. Since T defines an abelian group on $(\Pi, 0)$ and its restriction to the lines through 0 coincides with the addition, we shall write $x \, T \, y$ as $x + y$.

Corollary 12.4. Let x, y, y' be three non-collinear points. Let D be the line parallel to $\Delta(x, y')$ through y, and D' the line parallel to $\Delta(x, y)$ through y'. Then,

$$((x, y, x', y') \text{ is a parallelogram}) \Leftrightarrow (x' = D \cap D')$$

This is an immediate consequence of the third part of Theorem 12.3 when we take x as origin.

Corollary 12.5. (a is mid-point of (x, y)) $\Leftrightarrow$ ($x + y = a + a = 2a$.)

From this, we see that the symmetry with centre a is the map $x \to 2a - x$, and that the product of the symmetries with centres a and b is the translation $x \to 2(b - a) + x$ of $(\Pi, 0)$. Furthermore, any product of central symmetries and translations of $(\Pi, 0)$ is either a central symmetry or a translation depending on whether the number of those factors which are symmetries is odd or even.

Remark. The ordered structure of the plane was not used at all in the proof of Theorem 12.3, only the ordering of individual lines. As we might expect, the theorem could be proved from weaker axioms and such axioms will be found in an appendix.

Translations of Π

13. CHARACTERIZATION OF TRANSLATIONS

Lemma 13.1. 1. *In $(\Pi, 0)$, the mid-point of a pair (a, a') is the unique point p given by $2p = a + a'$.*

2. *$((a, b, a', b')$ is a parallelogram) $\Leftrightarrow$ ($a + a' = b + b'$).*

The first part comes from the definition of addition, the second from the fact that $(2p = 2q) \Leftrightarrow (p = q)$.

Corollary. 1. *Translations preserve mid-points.*

2 + G.I.A.M.S.

2. *Translations preserve parallelograms.*

This is true because the implication

$$(2m = x + y) \Rightarrow (2(m + a) = (x + a) + (y + a))$$

establishes that if (a, a') and (b, b') have the same mid-point, then so do their images under a translation.

Proposition 13.2. A mapping f from Π into itself is a translation of the group $(\Pi, 0)$ if and only if $(x, f(x), f(y), y)$ is a parallelogram for all x, y.

Proof. If f is the translation $x \to x + a$,

$$x + f(y) = f(x) + y, \quad \text{because} \quad x + (y + a) = (x + a) + y$$

Conversely, if f is such that $x + f(y) = f(x) + y$, for all x, y, then putting $x = 0$, we have

$$f(y) = f(0) + y$$

proving that f is a translation. This shows that the notion of a translation is independent of the choice of origin. In particular:

Corollary. For $a, b \in \Pi$, any translation of the group (Π, a) is also a translation of the group (Π, b).

14. ISOMORPHISM OF THE GROUPS $(\Pi, 0)$

Proposition 14.1. The translations of $(\Pi, 0)$ are a simply transitive group of transformations of Π. Denoting this group by $\mathscr{T}$, we have an isomorphism from $(\Pi, 0)$ onto $\mathscr{T}$, given by $a \to$ (translation $t_a : x \to x + a$).

2. *Let $a, b \in \Pi$. Then, if f is the translation taking a to b, $x \to f(x)$ is an isomorphism from (Π, a) onto (Π, b).*

Proof. 1. This is true of any group. Let us prove it once again. Let f_a be the translation $x \to x + a$ of $(\Pi, 0)$.

The map $a \to f_a$ must be injective because if $a \neq b$, $f_a(0) \neq f_b(0)$.

Also $f_{a+b}(x) = x + (a + b) = (x + a) + b = f_b(f_a(x)) = f_b \circ f_a(x)$, showing that $a \to f_a$ is a homomorphism. Thus it is an isomorphism.

2. In the first instance f is clearly a bijection of (Π, a) onto (Π, b). Let T and $\perp$ denote addition in (Π, a) and (Π, b) respectively.

But, for $x, y \in \Pi$, $(a, x, x \mathsf{T} y, y)$ is a parallelogram. Hence (corollary to 13.1), so is $(b, f(x), f(x \mathsf{T} y), f(y))$, and this proves that

$$f(x \mathsf{T} y) = f(x) \perp f(y)$$

15. FREE VECTORS AND CHASLES' FORMULA

Definition 15.1. Let $x, y \in \Pi$. The translation of Π taking x to y is called the free vector associated with the pair (x, y). It is generally denoted by $\overrightarrow{xy}$.

In the language of free vectors, composition of translations becomes additive.

For all $x, y, z \in \Pi$, $\overrightarrow{xy} + \overrightarrow{yz} = \overrightarrow{xz}$. This simply expresses the fact that the product of the translation taking x to y with that taking y to z is the translation taking x to z.

In general,

$$\overrightarrow{x_1 x_2} + \overrightarrow{x_2 x_3} + \cdots + \overrightarrow{x_{n-1} x_n} = \overrightarrow{x_1 x_n} \quad \text{(Chasles' formula)}$$

In particular, $\overrightarrow{xx}$ is the identity translation written 0, and so

$$\overrightarrow{xy} + \overrightarrow{yx} = 0 \quad \text{or} \quad \overrightarrow{xy} = -\overrightarrow{yx}$$

Notice that in $(\Pi, 0)$,

$$\overrightarrow{xy} = \overrightarrow{(x + z)(y + z)} \quad \text{for all } x, y, z$$

and, in particular,

$$\overrightarrow{xy} = \overrightarrow{0(y - x)}$$

Often, when calculating, it is convenient to identify the set of free vectors of Π with the elements of the group $(\Pi, 0)$. However, we must never forget that the two sets are not the same, only isomorphic.

16. ACTION OF TRANSLATIONS ON ORIENTATED LINES

The fourth part of Theorem 12.3 shows that the set $\mathscr{D}_\delta$ of lines with direction δ is stable under the translations, and that the action of the translations on this set is transitive.

We now examine the effect of a translation on an orientated line.

Proposition 16.1. Let D *be an orientated line, and* f *a translation.*

If $f(D) = D$, f *is in order isomorphism of* D *on to itself.*

If $f(D) \neq D$, f *is either an isomorphism or an anti-isomorphism of* D *onto* $f(D)$ *depending on which ordering is chosen on* $f(D)$.

Proof. If $f(D) = D$, the restriction of f to D is a translation of D and so is monotone non-decreasing.

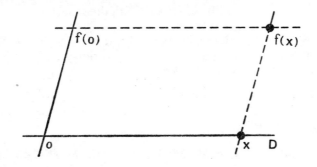

If $f(D) \neq D$, let 0 be a point of D. Now $f(0)$ cannot be on D, and $(0, x, f(x), f(0))$ is a parallelogram for every $x \in D$. Hence $\Delta(x, f(x)) \parallel \Delta(0, f(0))$, and the restriction of f to D is simply the oblique projection onto $f(D)$ parallel to $\Delta(0, f(0))$.

Applying Corollary 6.3, f is either an isomorphism or an anti-isomorphism of D onto $f(D)$ depending on how $f(D)$ is orientated.

Notice that $f(D)$ can always be orientated so as to make f an isomorphism.

Definition 16.2. We say that two orientated lines D, D' *are* parallel with same sense (*written* D $\uparrow\uparrow$ D') *if there is a translation f mapping* D *onto* D' *isomorphically.*

Proposition 16.3. 1. *The relation $\uparrow\uparrow$ is an equivalence relation on the set of orientated lines.*

2. *For every direction δ, the set $\mathscr{D}'_\delta$ of orientated lines with direction δ is the union of two equivalence classes. The two orientated lines obtainable from a given line belong to different classes.*

Proof. 1. This follows because inverses and products of order isomorphisms are order isomorphisms.

2. The translations act transitively on the set $\mathscr{D}_\delta$. Hence, 16.1 shows that $\mathscr{D}'_\delta$ is the union of at most two classes. On the other hand, if D_1, D_2 are the two orientated lines obtainable from some line with direction δ, Prop. 16.1 also shows that no translation takes D_1 to D_2. Thus D_1 and D_2 are in different classes, and $\mathscr{D}'_\delta$ is the union of two classes. This proves the result.

Corollary 16.4. If two orientated lines D, D' *are parallel with the same sense, a translation taking* D *to* D' *is an order isomorphism of* D *onto* D'.

When two orientated lines are parallel without having the same sense, we say that they have *opposite senses*.

Applications

16.5. *Orientated directions.* The orientated directions of Π are the classes of the equivalence relation $\uparrow\uparrow$ on the set $\mathscr{D}'$ of orientated lines.

16.6. *Translates of half-lines*

Consider the set of closed half-lines of Π and define A $\sim$ B if there is a translation f such that $f(A) = B$.

If this is so, we say that A and B are parallel with the same sense.

This is clearly an equivalence relation.

Using the definition of half-lines and Prop. 16.1, it is not too difficult to show that the image of a half-line originating at a under a translation f is a half-line originating at $f(a)$. It is then an easy step to derive the equivalence

(A $\sim$ B) $\Leftrightarrow$ (the lines associated with A and B are parallel with the same sense).

16.7. TRANSLATES OF INTERVALS

The interval $[a, b]$ is the intersection of the half-lines $D(a, b)$, $D(b, a)$. Hence, if f is a

translation, $f([a, b])$ is the intersection of the half-lines $D(f(a), f(b))$, $D(f(b), f(a))$ and is $[f(a), f(b)]$. Similar results hold for open and half-open intervals.

It naturally follows from this that the translates of convex sets are also convex.

(Π, 0) as a vector space

17. DEFINITIONS AND SCALAR MULTIPLICATION

Recall that a vector space over R is an abelian group E with a binary operator $(\lambda, x) \to \lambda x$, called scalar multiplication, from R × E into E satisfying:

(1) $$\lambda(x + y) = \lambda x + \lambda y$$

(2) $$(\lambda + \mu)x = \lambda x + \mu x$$

(3) $$\lambda(\mu x) = (\lambda\mu)x$$

(4) $$1x = x$$

for all $x, y \in E$ and $\lambda, \mu \in R$.

Up to now, we have only an abelian group structure on $(\Pi, 0)$ and the scalar multiplication remains to be defined. We proceed from the fact that each individual pointed line is already a vector space over R.

Definition 17. In the pointed plane $(\Pi, 0)$, the map $(\lambda, x) \to \lambda x$ from R × Π into Π is defined as follows:

1. $\lambda 0 = 0$.

2. *If $x \neq 0$, λx is the product of x by λ in the vector space consisting of the pointed line $\Delta(0, x)$ with origin 0. This mapping is called the* scalar multiplication of the pointed plane $(\Pi, 0)$.

Properties

Let us verify (2), (3), (4).

For $x = 0$, this is trivial.

For $x \neq 0$, they are true because they involve only the vector space $\Delta(0, x)$ (see consequence (3) of Prop. 9.1).

Notice that $(-1)x = -x$, the point symmetric to x about 0.

18. LINEARITY OF OBLIQUE PARALLEL PROJECTIONS

Before we can verify (1), we need the following lemma called Thales theorem (in France).

Lemma 18.1. If the line D passes through 0, and δ is a direction other than that of D, then, for all $x \in \Pi$, $\lambda \in R$, the oblique projection on D parallel to δ satisfies

(5) $$\varphi(\lambda x) = \lambda\varphi(x)$$

Let us first prove this for rational λ.

Now, for any integer $n \geqslant 0$, the relation $nx = \underbrace{x + x + \cdots + x}_{n\text{-times}}$ shows that

(6) $$\varphi(nx) = n\varphi(x)$$

Because $(-n)u = -(nu)$ and $\varphi(-u) = -\varphi(u)$, (6) can be extended to all integers n.

Again, if x is of the form $\frac{1}{n}y$ (where $n \neq 0$), (6) becomes

$$\varphi(y) = n\varphi\left(\frac{1}{n}y\right) \quad \text{giving} \quad \varphi\left(\frac{1}{n}y\right) = \frac{1}{n}\varphi(y)$$

and this shows that, for all integers p, q ($q \neq 0$),

$$\varphi\left(\frac{p}{q}x\right) = \varphi\left(p\left(\frac{1}{q}x\right)\right) = p\varphi\left(\frac{1}{q}x\right) = p\left(\frac{1}{q}\varphi(x)\right) = \frac{p}{q}\varphi(x)$$

valid for all $x \in \Pi$. Thus (5) is true for all rational λ.

Suppose now $x \neq 0$ (the case $x = 0$ is trivial).

If the direction of $\Delta(0, x)$ is δ, then as $\varphi(\lambda x) = 0$ for every λ, in this case, (5) follows immediately. Hence we may assume $\varphi(x) \neq 0$ and orientate the lines $\Delta(0,x)$ and D in such a way that $0 < x$ on $\Delta(0, x)$ and $0 < \varphi(x)$ on D.

Now the map $\lambda \rightarrow \lambda x$ from R on to $\Delta(0, x)$ is monotone increasing, as is the map $y \rightarrow \varphi(y)$ from $\Delta(0, x)$ onto D (Corollary 6.3). It follows that $\lambda \rightarrow \varphi(\lambda x)$ is monotone increasing, so is $\lambda \rightarrow \lambda\varphi(x)$, and we have just shown that these maps coincide on all rational λ. We now argue that the equality of the two maps is a well-known property of R, which can be assumed at this stage.

Corollary. For all $\lambda \in R$, $x, y \in \Pi$,

(1) $$\lambda(x + y) = \lambda x + \lambda y$$

Proof. If x, y are collinear with 0, this follows because the pointed line (D, 0) is a vector space.

If not, $\Delta(0, x)$ and $\Delta(0, y)$ are distinct, and it is sufficient to show that both sides of (1) have the same components in the system of axes formed by them.

However, if we let φ be the projection on $\Delta(0, x)$ parallel to $\Delta(0, y)$, Lemma 18.1 shows that $\varphi(\lambda(x + y)) = \lambda\varphi(x + y) = \lambda x$, while the fact that $\lambda x \in \Delta(0, x)$ and $\lambda y \in \Delta(0, y)$ gives $\varphi(\lambda x + \lambda y) = \lambda x$ also.

This shows that both sides of (1) have the same component on $\Delta(0, x)$, and a similar argument holds for $\Delta(0, y)$. In this way, the result follows.

19. THE VECTOR SPACE THEOREM

Theorem 19.1. Under the addition and scalar multiplication just defined, the pointed plane $(\Pi, 0)$ is a vector space over R of dimension 2. Any one dimensional affine subspace is a line of Π, and conversely.

Proof. We have just shown that $(\Pi, 0)$ is a vector space. Moreover, for $a \neq 0$, $\Delta(0, a)$ is

simply the set of points λa (where $\lambda \in R$). As $(\Pi, 0)$ is the direct sum of any two distinct lines through 0, its dimension must be 2.

We already know that any line in Π is the translate of some line through 0. The equivalence of lines and one-dimensional affine subspaces readily follows from this.

Application 19.2. Because $(\Pi, 0)$ is now a vector space, relation (5) of Lemma 18.1 and the additivity of φ imply:

> *The oblique parallel projection φ from $(\Pi, 0)$ onto $(D, 0)$ is a linear mapping.*

20. BASES AND COORDINATES. EQUATION OF A LINE

In accordance with the general theory of vector spaces, we shall call a pair (a_1, a_2) of elements of Π, a *basis* for the pointed plane $(\Pi, 0)$ if they are distinct from 0 and not collinear with 0.

Every x in Π then has a unique expression

$$x = \xi_1 a_1 + \xi_2 a_2$$

The scalars ξ_1 and ξ_2 are called the *coordinates* of x relative to the basis (a_1, a_2). We also say that $\xi_1 a_1$ and $\xi_2 a_2$ are the components of x relative to the system of axes $(\Delta(0, x),$ $\Delta(0, y))$. For any two scalars ξ_1, ξ_2 we let (ξ_1, ξ_2) denote the point x with coordinates ξ_1, ξ_2.

1. Let D be a line parallel to $\Delta(0, a_2)$ meeting $\Delta(0, a_1)$ at a point whose first coordinate is α_1. Then, clearly,

$$(x \in D) \Leftrightarrow (\xi_1 = \alpha_1)$$

with a similar result holding for lines parallel to $\Delta(0, a_1)$.

2. Let D be a line through 0 other than $\Delta(0, a_1)$ and $\Delta(0, a_2)$. Let $b = (\beta_1, \beta_2)$ be a point of D other than 0. Then

$$(x \in D) \Leftrightarrow (x \text{ is } \lambda b, \text{ where } \lambda \in R) \Leftrightarrow \left(\frac{\xi_1}{\beta_1} = \frac{\xi_2}{\beta_2} \right)$$

The ratio β_2/β_1 is called the *slope* of D relative to the given basis.

3. Finally, let D be any line not parallel to the axes.

For $a = (\alpha_1, \alpha_2)$ on D, the line $(D - a)$ passes through 0. Thus, taking (β_1, β_2) to be a point of $(D - a)$ other than 0, we have

$$(x \in D) \Leftrightarrow \left(\frac{\xi_1 - \alpha_1}{\beta_1} = \frac{\xi_2 - \alpha_2}{\beta_2} \right)$$

From these results, we easily deduce that any line in Π has an equation of the form $u\xi_1 + v\xi_2 + w = 0$, where u, v are not both zero. Moreover any equation of this form represents a line.

21. CHARACTERIZATION OF HOMOTHETIC TRANSFORMATIONS

In the course of studying the group $(\Pi, 0)$, we obtained an intrinsic characterization of the translations which enabled us to show that any two of the groups (Π, a), (Π, b) are

isomorphic. Our aim now is to extend this result to take account of the scalar multiplication.

Definition 21.1. *The* homothetic transformation with centre 0 and proportionality ratio k $(k \neq 0)$, *is that map from* Π *into itself which, in* $(\Pi, 0)$, *takes the form* $x \to kx$.

We shall write $H(0, k)$ for this map and, for every subset $X \subset \Pi$, we shall write kX for the set of elements kx with $x \in X$. Clearly, for every $0 \in \Pi$, and every $k \in R$ $(k \neq 0)$, there is a homothetic transformation with 0 as its centre and k as its ratio.

The following properties follow immediately.

1. The product of the maps $x \to kx$ and $y \to \frac{1}{k} y$ is the identity. Thus $H(0, k)$ is a non-singular transformation of Π with inverse $H(0, 1/k)$.

2. $$k(X + a) = kX + ka$$

3. If $k \neq 1$,

$$(x = kx) \Leftrightarrow ((1 - k)x = 0) \Leftrightarrow (x = 0)$$

Thus the only fixed point of a homothetic transformation of ratio $k \neq 1$ is the centre.

Proposition 21.2. *A map f from* Π *into itself is a homothetic transformation with centre 0 if and only if* $f(0) = 0$ *and every line* D *is mapped by f onto a parallel line.*

Proof. 1. Let f be the homothetic transformation $x \to kx$. Then, clearly, $f(0) = 0$ and $f(D) = D$ whenever D passes through 0.

If D is an arbitrary line, we know that $D = D' + a$, where D' is parallel to D and passes through 0, and a is any point of D. It follows that

$$f(D) = kD = k(D' + a) = kD' + ka = D' + ka$$

and this proves that $f(D)$ is parallel to D' and therefore D.

2. Conversely, suppose f is such that $f(0) = 0$ and $f(D)$ is always parallel to D. We see immediately that if D passes through 0, $f(D) = D$ and for every point $x \neq 0$ in Π, there is some scalar λ_x such that $f(x) = \lambda_x x$. Obviously, we need to show that λ_x is a non-zero scalar independent of x.

Let A, B be a pair of distinct lines through 0. As $f(A) = A$, there must be $a \in A$ $(a \neq 0)$ such that $f(a) \neq 0$, i.e. $\lambda_a \neq 0$. Write g for the homothetic transformation $H(0, \lambda_a)$.

If $b \in B$, B and $\Delta(a, b)$ cut at b and so their images under f cut at $f(b)$. However, these images are respectively B and the line parallel to $\Delta(a, b)$ through $f(a) = \lambda_a a$, and these coincide with the images of B and $\Delta(a, b)$ under g.

Hence $f(b) = g(b) = \lambda_a(b)$, proving that $\lambda_b = \lambda_a$ for every $b \in B$.

By interchanging the roles of A and B, we also have $\lambda_a = \lambda_b$ for all $a \in A$, $b \in B$, proving that λ_x is constant on $A \cup B$. But A, B were arbitrarily chosen lines through 0. Thus λ_x is a non-zero constant, for all $x \in \Pi$, and this proves the result.

Corollary 21.3. *In* $(\Pi, 0)$, *the map f defined by*

$$x \to k(x - a) + a \quad (where\ a \in \Pi,\ k \in R^*)$$

is the homothetic transformation $H(a, k)$.

The map f is a product of translations and homothetic transformations. Consequently, lines are mapped into parallel lines. On the other hand $f(a) = a$, and so f is a homothetic transformation with centre a.

If $a = 0$, $f = H(0, k)$, obviously.

If $a \neq 0$, the line $\Delta(0, a)$ is stabilized by f and on this line the relation

$$y = k(x - a) + a$$

becomes $ay = k\overline{ax}$, showing that the ratio is indeed k.

The above corollary can also be stated as follows:

Corollary 21.4. Let (a, x), (b, y) be two pairs of points of Π such that $\overrightarrow{ax} = \overrightarrow{by}$. If x', y' are the images of x, y under the respective transformations $H(a, k)$, $H(b, k)$, then $\overrightarrow{ax'} = \overrightarrow{by'}$.

Remark. Prop. 21.2 could be expanded to give:

A homothetic transformation of positive (resp. negative) ratio maps any line onto a line which is parallel with the same (resp. opposite) sense.

This is clear for lines through the centre of the transformation. The general case is obtained by applying two translations and remembering that these preserve senses.

22. Isomorphism of the vector spaces $(\Pi, 0)$

Proposition 22.1. Let a, $b \in \Pi$ and let f be the translation taking a to b. Then the map $x \to f(x)$ is an isomorphism between the space (Π, a) and the space (Π, b).

By 14.1, we already know that f is an isomorphism for the additive structure of these spaces. All we need do is derive the property

$$f(\lambda . x) = \lambda * f(x)$$

where . and * denote scalar products in (Π, a), (Π, b) respectively.

Writing $+$ for addition in (Π, a), we see that f is given by

$$f(u) = u + b \quad \text{showing that} \quad f(\lambda . x) = \lambda . x + b$$

Similarly, by Corollary 21.3 above,

$$\lambda * f(x) = \lambda . (f(x) - b) + b = \lambda x + b$$

thereby giving the required result.

23. Translations as a vector space

Let $0 \in \Pi$ and, for every $a \in (\Pi, 0)$, let t_a be the translation $x \to (x + a)$ of $(\Pi, 0)$. Prop. 14 shows that the map $\varphi_0 : a \to t_a$ is an isomorphism between the additive structure of $(\Pi, 0)$ and the group $\mathscr{T}$ of translations. We can obviously use φ_0 to turn $\mathscr{T}$ into a vector space which is isomorphic to $(\Pi, 0)$ as a vector space.

This structure defined on $\mathscr{T}$ is independent of the choice of origin 0; so much is clear from Prop. 22.1. In other words, we have turned the set of free vectors of Π into a vector space in such a way that, for any $0 \in \Pi$, the map $\overrightarrow{0x} \to x$ is an isomorphism between this vector space and the space $(\Pi, 0)$.

2*

5. Dilations of the plane

24. CHARACTERIZATION OF DILATIONS

Definition 24.1. A transformation of Π which, in some pointed plane $(\Pi, 0)$, takes the form $x \to kx + a$ (where k is a non-zero scalar) is called a dilation of Π.

Clearly, if a transformation takes the form $x \to kx + a$ in one pointed plane, it takes a similar form in every pointed plane. Any dilation is the product of a homothetic transformation and a translation.

Proposition 24.2. A map f is a dilation of Π if and only if it maps every line D on to a line parallel to D.

Proof. Take an origin 0 in Π. Since f is of the form $x \to kx + a$, $(k \ne 0)$, it is the product of a homothetic transformation and a translation and must therefore map every line onto a parallel line.

On the other hand, if f has this last property, then the map $x \to f(x) - f(0)$ also has the property and it also fixes 0. By Prop. 21.2, it is $H(0, k)$ for some k and this proves that $f(x) = kx + f(0)$.

Proposition 24.3. Let f be the dilation defined in $(\Pi, 0)$ by $x \to kx + a$. Then, if $k = 1$, it is a translation, otherwise it is a homothetic transformation of ratio k.

This is true because if $k \ne 1$, the equation $x = f(x)$ has a solution

$$x_0 = \left(\frac{1}{1-k}\right) a$$

showing that f is $H(x_0, k)$ (Corollary 21.3).

The number k is called the *proportionality ratio* or *ratio* of the dilation.

From the relation $x_0 = \left(\frac{1}{1-k}\right) a$, we see that a translation $x \to x + a$ can be thought of as a limit of homothetic transformations whose centres tend to infinity along the line $\Delta(0, a)$ and whose ratios tend to 1. Although phrased somewhat vaguely, this statement could easily be given a precise and rigorous meaning.

25. THE DILATION GROUP

Let f, f' be the dilations given, in $(\Pi, 0)$, by

$$x \to kx + a \qquad x \to k'x + a' \quad \text{respectively}$$

It is easy to verify that:

1. The inverse of f is the dilation $x \to \left(\frac{1}{k}\right) x - \left(\frac{1}{k}\right) a$.

2. $f' \circ f$ is the dilation $x \to k'kx + (k'a + a')$ of ratio $k'k$.

3. $(f' \circ f = f \circ f') \Leftrightarrow (k'a + a' = ka' + a) \Leftrightarrow ((1 - k)a' = (1 - k')a)$.

Thus, for commutativity, either f or f' is the identity,
       or both f and f' are translations,

       or both $k \neq 1$, $k' \neq 1$ and $\dfrac{1}{(1 - k)} a = \dfrac{1}{(1 - k')} a'$

(i.e. f and f' are homothetic transformations with the same centre).

4. If D is a line such that $f(D) = D$ and $f'(D) = D$, then $f' \circ f(D) = D$ also.

Thus, if f and f' are homothetic transformations with centres 0, $0'$ $(0 \neq 0')$, $f' \circ f$ (and $f \circ f'$) is either a homothetic transformation with centre on $\Delta(0, 0')$ or is a translation parallel to $\Delta(0, 0')$.

In a similar manner, if f is a homothetic transformation with centre 0, and f' is the translation $x \to x + a$ $(a \neq 0)$, $f' \circ f$ and $f \circ f'$ are both homothetic transformations with centre on $\Delta(0, a)$.

All these results are essentially summarized by the following:

Proposition 25.1. The dilations of Π form a non-abelian group of transformations under composition. Denoting this group by $\mathcal{G}$, we can say that two elements of $\mathcal{G}$ commute only if they are both translations or both homothetic transformations with the same centre.

Furthermore, the map $f \to k(f)$, where $k(f)$ is the ratio of f, is a homomorphism of $\mathcal{G}$ into R^*.

26. Subgroups of the Dilation Group

1. For $a \in \Pi$, the set $\mathcal{H}(a)$ of homothetic transformations with centre a is an abelian subgroup of $\mathcal{G}$ isomorphic to R^*. There is a subgroup of $\mathcal{H}(a)$ corresponding to every subgroup M of R^*. The case $M = \{1, -1\}$ gives rise to the group consisting of the identity and the central symmetry about a $(x \to 2a - x)$. The case $M = R^*_+$ gives the group of *positive homothetic transformations* with centre a. Other cases which might be mentioned are

$$M = Q \quad \text{and} \quad M = \{k^n\}_{n \in Z} \quad \text{(where } k \neq 0)$$

2. The translation group $\mathcal{T}$, and all its subgroups. When studying $\mathcal{T}$, it is useful to remember that it is isomorphic to the additive group R^2. Interesting subgroups correspond to the subgroups $Z \times \{0\}$, $Z \times Z$, $Z \times R$ of R^2 under this isomorphism; e.g. corresponding to $Z \times Z$ we have the set of translations of the form $pa + qb$ where $p, q \in Z$ and a, b are a fixed but arbitrary pair of points of Π not collinear with 0.

3. Let φ be the homomorphism $f \to k(f)$ of Prop. 25.1.

If M is any subgroup of R^*, $\varphi^{-1}(M)$ is a normal subgroup of $\mathcal{G}$.

For $M = \{1\}$, $\varphi^{-1}(M)$ is the translation group.

For $M = \{1, -1\}$, $\varphi^{-1}(M)$ is the group of translations and central symmetries.

For $M = R^*_+$, $\varphi^{-1}(M)$ is the group of dilations preserving the sense of orientated lines.

27. Dilations of Subsets of Π

In any presentation of elementary geometry, it is usual to study homothetic triangles,

i.e. pairs of triangles which can be mapped one to the other by a dilation. Here, we shall study the effect of dilations on an arbitrary subset of Π.

Lemma 27.1. If u, v, u', $v' \in \Pi$ are such that

$$u \neq v, \quad u' \neq v' \quad \text{and} \quad \Delta(u, v) \parallel \Delta(u', v')$$

then there is a unique dilation f mapping u to u' and v to v'.

Proof. 1. *Existence.* There is a translation taking (u, v) to (u', v'') and a homothetic transformation then taking (u', v'') to (u', v'). The product of these produces the required result.

2. *Uniqueness.* If f and g are solutions, $f^{-1} \circ g$ is a dilation with u and v as fixed points. Writing $f^{-1} \circ g$ in the form $x \to kx + a$, we have

$$ku + a = u \quad \text{and} \quad kv + a = v, \quad \text{or} \quad (1 - k)(u - v) = 0$$

Hence, $k = 1$ and $a = 0$, showing that $f^{-1} \circ g$ is the identity, or $f = g$.

Proposition 27.2. Let X be a non-empty, non-collinear subset of Π and let f be a mapping from X into Π such that $\Delta(f(x), f(y)) \parallel \Delta(x, y)$, for all pairs (x, y) of distinct elements of X. Then, either $f(x)$ is a single point or f is the restriction to X of some (unique) dilation of Π.

Proof. Case 1. f has at least two fixed points a, b.

If $x \in X$ but $x \notin \Delta(a, b)$, the lines $\Delta(a, x)$ and $\Delta(b, x)$ cut and are parallel to $\Delta(a, f(x))$, $\Delta(b, f(x))$ respectively.

Thus $f(x) = x$ and f is the identity outside $\Delta(a, b)$.

Now, by hypothesis, there is at least one point $c \notin \Delta(a, b)$. The same reasoning applies to $\Delta(a, c)$, showing that f is the identity outside $\Delta(a, c)$. As f is identity outside $\Delta(a, b)$ and $\Delta(a, c)$, f is indeed the identity on X.

Case 2. We assume that $f(x)$ is not a single point and so there are points a, $b \in X$ such that $f(a) \neq f(b)$. Because $\Delta(a, b) \parallel \Delta(f(a), f(b))$, there exists, by Lemma 27.1, a dilation g such that $g(a) = f(a)$ and $g(b) = f(b)$. Now $g^{-1} \circ f$ is a map from X into Π satisfying the hypotheses of the proposition and has a, b as fixed points. By case 1, $g^{-1} \circ f$ is the identity on X, proving that f is the restriction of g to X. The uniqueness of g is apparent from Lemma 27.1 above.

Remark. If X is collinear, any map f from X into a line parallel to that containing X satisfies the required properties. The assumption that X is not collinear cannot be omitted.

6. Further results

28. A FEW TOPICS FOR CONSIDERATION

1. Affine transformations of the plane: these are defined as the mappings of the form $x \to l(x) + a$, where l is a linear transformation of $(\Pi, 0)$ into itself satisfying $(l(x) = 0) \Rightarrow (x = 0)$. They can be classified as the transformations of Π which map lines on to lines.

2. In general, we can study affine maps from a plane Π into another plane Π'.

An intuitive idea of what is involved is easily given by taking a rectangular network of Π and considering its image under f in Π'. Several examples occur in nature, such as the shadow of a sunlit window on the floor, vertical projection of one plane onto a horizontal plane, deformation of trelliswork, etc.

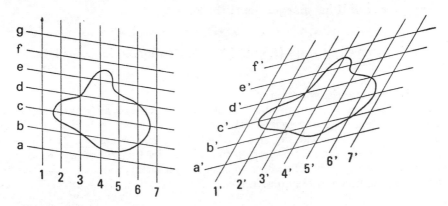

3. Affine mappings of a plane onto a line, and linear forms. Affine mappings of R into a plane (parametrization of lines in Π).

4. Barycentres. Invariance under affine maps; applications to convex sets.

29. OBLIQUE SYMMETRY

By means of an example, we shall show how oblique symmetries can be analysed using very elementary methods.

Definition 29.1. Let A be a line and δ a direction other than that of A. The oblique symmetry parallel to δ having axis A is the map $x \rightarrow f(x)$, where $f(x)$ is that point on the line through x with direction δ such that the mid-point of $(x, f(x))$ is on A.

Clearly f^2 is the identity and so f is an involutory transformation of Π.

Next let B be any line with direction δ and suppose B cuts A at 0. Let x_1, x_2 denote the components of the point x in the system of axes (A, B). The components of $f(x)$ are then x_1 and $-x_2$ (this also proves that f is a linear transformation of $(\Pi, 0)$). In a similar way, if g is the oblique symmetry parallel to A with axis B, $g(x)$ has components $-x_1$ and x_2.

Thus $f \circ g = g \circ f$, both products being the central symmetry h given by

$$(x_1, x_2) \rightarrow (-x_1, -x_2)$$

whose centre is clearly 0.

Conversely, if the product of two oblique symmetries is the symmetry whose centre is 0, then it is clear that they are the oblique symmetries arising from a pair of lines cutting at 0. Such symmetries are called *conjugate*.

The relation $g \circ f = f \circ g = h$ can also be written as $g = f \circ h = h \circ f$, and this

shows that the product of an oblique symmetry with axis D and a central symmetry whose centre is on D is an oblique symmetry which is conjugate with respect to the first.

Proposition 29.2. Every oblique symmetry transforms lines into lines.

Proof. With the preceding notation, take a basis (a, b) of $(\Pi, 0)$ such that $a \in A$, $b \in B$.

Every line D of Π has an equation of the form

$$u\xi + v\eta + w = 0 \quad \text{(where } u, v \text{ are not both zero)}$$

Now the symmetry f maps (ξ, η) to $(\xi, -\eta)$. Hence $f(D)$ has equation

$$u\xi - v\eta + w = 0$$

and this is obviously the equation of a line.

From this, we see that any product of oblique symmetries is an affine transformation of Π. It can be shown (see Exercises) that the set of such products is precisely the group of affine transformations with determinant ± 1 (i.e. area-preserving). This group plays an analogous role in the affine group to that played by the isometries in the group of similitudes. In other words, any affine transformation is the product of a positive homothetic transformation and oblique symmetries.

Exercises on Chapter II

1. Let A be a subset of Π, and let $0 \in \Pi$ be a centre of symmetry. Show that, if every line passing through 0 meets A in a non-zero finite number of points, 0 is the only centre of symmetry of A.

2. Let A be a subset of Π having a centre of symmetry, and let f be a dilation. Show that there exists another dilation $g \neq f$ such that $f(A) = g(A)$.

3. Let $(a_1, a_2, \ldots, a_n)$ be a finite sequence of points of Π. Determine the sequences $(x_1, x_2, \ldots, x_n)$ such that every pair (x_i, x_{i+1}) has a_i as mid-point (with the convention that $x_{n+1} = x_1$).

4. Let A be an arbitrary subset of Π. Show that the set X of centres of symmetry of A is symmetrical with respect to any of its points, and that X is closed when A is closed. Determine all the closed subsets X of Π which are symmetric with respect to each of their points.

5. Let $\delta_1, \delta_2, \delta_3$ be three distinct directions, and let A, B be two lines which are not parallel to δ_1.

For every line D_1 parallel to δ_1, let D_2 be the parallel to δ_2 taken through $A \cap D_1$, and let D_3 be the parallel to δ_3 taken through $B \cap D_1$.

Let $f(D_1) = D_2 \cap D_3$.

What is the set of all $f(D_1)$?

6. Let (A, B), (A', B') be two pairs of lines such that $A \parallel A'$, $B \parallel B'$. Determine all dilations which transform $A \cup B$ into $A' \cup B'$.

7. Let A, B be two bounded subsets of Π. Show that there exist at most two dilations f of Π such that $f(A) = B$.

8. Let f be a mapping of Π into Π and let δ be the direction of a line. Show that, if for all $x, y \in \Pi$, where $x \neq y$, the points $f(x), f(y)$ belong to a line parallel to $\Delta(x, y)$, and if for every $x \in \Pi$, the points $x, f(x)$ belong to a line with direction δ, then f is a translation.

9. Dilations of R.

(a) We can identify the dilation $x \rightarrow kx + a$ of R with the point (k, a) of $\mathbf{R}^2$. The group $\mathscr{G}$ of dilations of R is thus identified with a subset of $\mathbf{R}^2$. $\mathscr{G}$ is given the topology induced by that of $\mathbf{R}^2$ in this identification.

What are the images in $\mathbf{R}^2$ of the subgroups of $\mathscr{G}$ corresponding to (1) the homothetic transformations with centre at x_0, (2) the translations?

(b) Show that if a subgroup $\mathscr{G}'$ of $\mathscr{G}$ contains a homothetic transformation $H(x_0, k)$ where $k \neq +1$ or -1, and a dilation f such that $f(x_0) \neq x_0$, the set of centres of the homothetic transformation of ratio k of $\mathscr{G}'$ is dense throughout R. Deduce that if $\mathscr{G}'$ is closed, it contains all translations of R.

10. Show that every oblique symmetry of Π has a determinant equal to -1. Show that every affine transformation of Π with determinant -1 or 1 is a product of 3 or 4 oblique symmetries (argue as in the proof of Theorem 45.6).

11. Determine all the closed groups of linear transformation of $(\Pi, 0)$ which operate in a simply transitive manner on $\Pi - \{0\}$.

Chapter III

Axioms for metric structure

1. Perpendiculars

30. PERPENDICULARITY AXIOM

Distances were used in formulating Axiom III simply to introduce the affine structure on the lines. The plane defined by Axioms I, II, III has no truly metric structure because, even though each line has a metric, there is no Axiom linking the metrics of various lines. Axiom III$_b$ involves only mid-points and has an affine character. The following remarks illustrate this.

Let Π be a plane satisfying Axioms I, II, III with distance function d. Let f be any mapping from the set $\mathcal{D}$ of lines in Π into $(0, \infty]$. For every $x, y \in \Pi$, with $x \neq y$, set

$$d'(x, y) = k_{x,y} d(x, y) \quad \text{where} \quad k_{x,y} = f(\Delta(x, y))$$

Clearly, even with the distance d', Π still satisfies Axioms I, II, III and, despite the fact that the distance on any given line has been multiplied by an arbitrary positive scalar depending only on that line, the affine structure remains the same.

We now link the metrics on the various lines using orthogonal projections. First, we must define what we mean by perpendicular lines.

Axiom IV$_a$ (perpendiculars)

Perpendicularity (written $\perp$) is a binary relation on the set $\mathcal{D}$ of lines of Π, such that

1. $(A \perp B) \Leftrightarrow (B \perp A)$ (symmetry).
2. $(A \perp B) \Rightarrow (A \text{ and } B \text{ not parallel})$.
3. For every line A, there is at least one line B with $A \perp B$.
4. For every pair (A, B) with $(A \perp B)$, and every line B'
$$(B \parallel B') \Leftrightarrow (A \perp B')$$

31. PERPENDICULAR DIRECTIONS

We shall say that two directions are perpendicular (and we shall write $\delta \perp \delta'$), if there exists two lines D, D′ with directions δ, δ' such that $D \perp D'$.

In this way, a binary relation is defined on the set **D** of directions, and, by Axiom IV_a, it is seen that the following properties P' hold:

1. Symmetry.
2. Anti-reflexivity ($\delta \perp \delta$ is impossible).
3. For every direction δ, there exists a unique δ' such that $\delta \perp \delta'$. Moreoever,

$$(D \perp D') \Leftrightarrow (\text{direction of } D \perp \text{direction of } D')$$

It is easily verified that the converse holds, in that every binary relation on the set **D** of directions, having the properties P', is the relation associated with some perpendicularity relation on the set $\mathscr{D}$ (put $D \perp D'$ if the directions of D and D' are perpendicular).

How general is the relation of perpendicularity?

The above point enables us to appreciate the degree of generality involved in the perpendicularity relations on $\mathscr{D}$ given by Axiom IV_a. Effectively, taking such a relation on $\mathscr{D}$ is equivalent to choosing a relation satisfying on **D** the properties P' and, in turn, this becomes a question of partitioning **D** into subsets each of which contains exactly two elements (making up a pair of perpendicular directions).

Because of this vast generality, Axiom IV_a would not really help us to study the metric properties of the plane if it were not completed by Axiom IV_b which brings in the distances. It is rather marvellous that despite its great simplicity, this latter axiom deals with all possible quirks of metric and perpendicularity in one clean sweep.

Comment. Axiom IV_a introduces perpendicularity as a primitive notion. We do not think that this presents any difficulty in teaching, because pupils will already have encountered the idea in different contexts: bending a sheet of paper over a straight edge; horizontal and vertical directions; shortest distance of a point from a line, etc.

32. AFFINE PROPERTIES WHICH ARE APPARENTLY METRIC

Despite its rather general nature, Axiom IV_a can be used to obtain easy proofs of several results which are usually not stated and proved until a more advanced stage of the development has been reached.

1. Every dilation preserves perpendicularity.
   This is clear, because if f is a dilation and $(D \perp D')$, then $D \parallel f(D)$ and $D' \parallel f(D')$. Thus

$$(D \perp D') \Rightarrow (f(D) \perp f(D'))$$

2. Consider the oblique symmetry whose axis is D and whose direction is perpendicular to that of D. This is known as symmetry with respect to D (or symmetry with axis D). Then,

Proposition 32.1. The product of the symmetries with respect to two perpendicular lines D, D' *is the central symmetry whose centre is* $D \cap D'$.

This is simply a special case of the proposition about a pair of oblique symmetries conjugate with respect to a pair of intersecting lines. Thus, despite appearances, it expresses a purely affine property.

33. Projection ratio of a pair of half-lines originating at the same point

The oblique projection on a line D whose direction is perpendicular to that of D is called the *orthogonal projection on* D.

Let A_1, A_2 be a pair of half-lines with the same origin in 0, and let D_1, D_2 be the lines containing them. We may assume that these are orientated so that $A_1 \geqslant 0$ and $A_2 \geqslant 0$.

For $x \in D_1$, we write $\overline{0x}$ for the algebraic (or signed) distance of $(0, x)$ on D_1 and similarly for D_2. We let φ be the orthogonal projection on D_1 and a be that point of A_2 such that $\overline{0a} = 1$.

Now for every $\lambda \in R$, we know that

$$\varphi(\lambda a) = \lambda \varphi(a)$$

and, as every $x \in D_2$ is of the form λa, we see that the ratio $\overline{0\varphi(x)}/\overline{0x}$ is independent of the choice of x on $D_2 - \{0\}$, being equal to $\overline{0\varphi(a)}$.

This enables us to make the following definition:

Definition 33.1. With the above notation, the scalar k such that $\overline{0\varphi(x)} = k\overline{0x}$ for all $x \in D_2$ is called the projection ratio of A_2 on A_1. *It is denoted by $c(A_1, A_2)$.*

Thus

$$c(A_1, A_2) = \overline{0\varphi(a)}$$

and

$$(c(A_1, A_2) = 0) \Leftrightarrow (\varphi(a) = 0) \Leftrightarrow (A_1 \perp A_2)$$

(where $(A_1 \perp A_2)$ means $(D_1 \perp D_2)$).

If $A_1 = A_2$, $c(A_1, A_2) = 1$, but if A_1 and A_2 are collinear and opposite, $c(A_1, A_2) = -1$. The converse of this does not follow from Axiom IV_a.

2. Inner product

34. Symmetry axiom

Axiom IV_b. For every pair (A_1, A_2) of half-lines with the same origin,

$$c(A_1, A_2) = c(A_2, A_1)$$

Equivalently, in a more elementary, but less instructive form:

If $(0, a, b)$ is a non-collinear triplet such that $d(0, a) = d(0, b)$, and if a' and b' denote the orthogonal projections of a and b on $\Delta(0, b)$ and $\Delta(0, a)$ respectively, then $\overline{0a'} = \overline{0b'}$ on the lines $\Delta(0, b)$ and $\Delta(0, a)$ respectively orientated so that $0 \leqslant b$ and $0 \leqslant a$.

35. Norm and inner product

Definition 35.1. In the pointed plane $(\Pi, 0)$, the norm of x (where $x \in \Pi$) is the positive number $\| x \| = d(0, x)$.

It is immediate that $\| x \|$ is non-zero unless $x = 0$, and that for every scalar λ, $\| \lambda x \| = | \lambda | \times \| x \|$. In particular, $\| - x \| = \| x \|$.

Definition 35.2. In the pointed plane $(\Pi, 0)$, *the inner product of the vectors x and y is the real number, written* $x.y$, *defined as follows:*

1. *If either or both of* x, y *are* 0,
$$x.y = 0$$

2. *If* $x \neq 0$ *and* $y \neq 0$, *and we put* $X = D(0, x)$, $Y = D(0, y)$,
$$x.y = \| x \| \times \| y \| \times c(X, Y)$$

It is often useful to write x^2 *for* $x.x$.

Immediate consequences

1. The relation $x.y = 0$ holds if and only if

$$\text{either } x \text{ or } y \text{ is } 0 \quad \text{or} \quad X \perp Y$$

For convenience, we shall say that the vectors x, y of $(\Pi, 0)$ are perpendicular (written $x \perp y$), if either x or y is 0, or if $x \neq 0$ and $y \neq 0$ with $X \perp Y$. With this convention,

$$(x.y = 0) \Leftrightarrow (x \perp y)$$

2. Let D be an arbitrary orientated line through 0 and x. If φ denotes the orthogonal projection on D, then

$$x.y = \overline{Ox} \times \overline{O(\varphi(y))}$$

This is trivial if either of x, y is 0. If not, then since a change of orientation does not affect the product $\overline{Ox} \times \overline{O(\varphi(y))}$, it is sufficient to prove the relation when D is the orientated line $\Delta(0, x)$. In this case,

$$\overline{Ox} = \| x \| \quad \text{and} \quad \overline{O\varphi(y)} = \| y \| \, c(X, Y), \quad \text{whence the result.}$$

Notation. In $(\Pi, 0)$ we shall sometimes write $c(x, y)$ for $c(X, Y)$; this only makes sense when $x \neq 0$ and $y \neq 0$.

Theorem 35.3. The mapping $(x, y) \to x.y$ *from* $(\Pi, 0) \times (\Pi, 0)$ *into* R *is symmetric and bilinear.*
    Furthermore, it is positive in the sense that $x.x > 0$ *for all* $x \neq 0$ *(in fact, for every* x, $x.x = \| x \|^2$).

Proof. 1. The relation $x.y = y.x$ is evident if either x or y is 0. If not, it comes from Definition 35.2 coupled with the equality $c(X, Y) = c(Y, X)$ given by Axiom IV$_b$.

2. For every x, the mapping $y \to x.y$ of $(\Pi, 0)$ into R is linear.

If $x = 0$, this is clear because $x.y = 0$, however y is chosen.
If $x \neq 0$, taking φ to be the orthogonal projection onto the orientated line $\Delta(0, x)$,

we see that the map $y \to \varphi(y)$ is a linear mapping from $(\Pi, 0)$ onto the pointed line $\Delta(0, x)$.

As the mapping $u \to \overline{0u}$ from $\Delta(0, x)$ into R is also linear, this means that the composition $y \to \overline{0\varphi(y)}$ is linear, as, then, is $y \to \overline{0x} \times \overline{0\varphi(y)} = x.y$. As $x.y = y.x$, this proves the bilinearity of the inner product.

3. Finally, the relation $x.x = \| x \|^2$ comes straight from the definition of the inner product.

36. IDENTITIES AND INEQUALITIES

The bilinearity and symmetry of the inner product makes calculations easy. We have the identity:

$$\left(\sum_i \alpha_i x_i \right) . \left(\sum_j \beta_j y_j \right) = \sum_{i,j} \alpha_i \beta_j \; x_i . x_j$$

In particular, we have the classical identities

$$(a + b)^2 = a^2 + b^2 + 2a.b$$
$$(a - b)^2 = a^2 + b^2 - 2a.b$$

Adding and subtracting:

$$(a + b)^2 + (a - b)^2 = 2(a^2 + b^2)$$
$$(a + b)^2 - (a - b)^2 = 4a.b$$

2. From the inner product, we obtain the following important identity.

Let x, y be two vectors of $(\Pi, 0)$ with $x, y \neq 0$. Now for every scalar λ,

$$(\lambda x - y)^2 = \lambda^2 x^2 - 2\lambda x.y + y^2 \geqslant 0$$

and as this quadratic in λ is positive for all λ, it has a non-positive discriminant. In other words, for all x, y,

$$(x.y)^2 \leqslant x^2 \times y^2 \quad \text{or} \quad | x.y | \leqslant \| x \| \times \| y \|$$

Equality can only hold if the quadratic in λ is zero. This can only be so when there is a λ such that $y = \lambda x$, implying that $0, x, y$ are collinear.

To sum up,

$$| x.y | < \| x \| \times \| y \| \quad \text{if } 0, x, y \text{ are not collinear}$$
$$x.y = \| x \| \times \| y \| \quad \text{if } y = \lambda x \text{ with } \lambda > 0$$
$$x.y = - \| x \| \times \| y \| \quad \text{if } y = \lambda x \text{ with } \lambda < 0$$

It is immediate that the last two equalities are also true if $x = 0$ or $y = 0$.

The relation $x.y = \| x \| \times \| y \| \times c(x,y)$ enables us to translate these results into the following proposition.

Proposition 36.1. For all vectors x, y of $(\Pi, 0)$ with $x \neq 0$ and $y \neq 0$,

$$(| c(x,y) | <) \; 1 \Leftrightarrow (0, x, y \text{ are not collinear})$$
$$(c(x,y) =) \; 1 \Leftrightarrow (\text{the half-lines } D(0, x) \text{ and } D(0, y) \text{ are the same})$$
$$(c(x,y) = -) \; 1 \Leftrightarrow (\text{the half-lines } D(0, x) \text{ and } D(0, y) \text{ are opposite})$$

37. INVARIANCE OF DISTANCE AND INNER PRODUCT UNDER TRANSLATION

The inner product that we have just defined apparently depends on the choice of origin 0. We shall show that it is really independent in a sense that will emerge later.

To make the proof more intuitive, we shall prove this independence by starting with the invariance of distance.

Definition 37.1. Any parallelogram (a, b, a', b') in which the equation $b.b' = 0$ holds in $(\Pi, 0)$, is called a rectangle. *(The equation $b.b' = 0$ can also be written as $b \perp b'$.)*

Lemma 37.2. In every rectangle the lengths of two opposite sides are equal.

Proof.

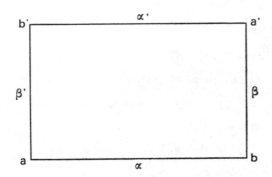

If the point a is taken as origin for Π, we have

$$a' = b + b' \quad \text{and} \quad b \perp b'$$

whence

$$a'^2 = (b + b')^2 = b^2 + b'^2 + 2b.b' = b^2 + b'^2$$

Thus

$$d^2(a, a') = d^2(a, b) + d^2(a, b')$$

The same reasoning applies to each vertex of the rectangle and, from this using the notation given in the diagram, we obtain the two equalities:

$$\alpha^2 + \beta^2 = \alpha'^2 + \beta'^2; \qquad \alpha^2 + \beta'^2 = \alpha'^2 + \beta^2$$

Adding and subtracting, we have

$$\alpha^2 = \alpha'^2 \quad \text{and} \quad \beta^2 = \beta'^2$$

and the result now follows.

This lemma can also be stated as follows:

For every line D and every translation f perpendicular to D, the restriction of f to D is an isometry (i.e. it preserves distances).

More generally:

Proposition 37.3. Every translation is an isometry.

Proof. Let $x, y \in \Pi$ and let f be the translation $u \to u + a$ of the plane $(\Pi, 0)$. We would like to show that

$$d(x, y) = d(f(x), f(y))$$

This is trivial if $x = y$.

If $x \neq y$, it is true when f is parallel to $\Delta(x, y)$ (because f maps $\Delta(x, y)$ onto itself), and when f is perpendicular to this line (above lemma).

Now let a_1, a_2 be the components of a with respect to two lines passing through 0, one parallel to $\Delta(x, y)$, the other perpendicular. Let f_i be the translation $u \to u + a_i$ $(i = 1, 2)$.

Because f is the product of the translations f_1, f_2 which are respectively parallel and perpendicular to $\Delta(x, y)$, it now follows that the distances of the pairs (x, y) and $(f(x), f(y))$ are indeed the same.

Corollary 37.4. In the plane $(\Pi, 0)$,

$$d^2(x, y) = \| y - x \|^2 = (x - y)^2 \quad \textit{for all } x, y \in \Pi$$

For, translated to $(\Pi, 0)$, prop. 37.3 states that

$$d(x, y) = d(x + a, y + a) \quad \text{for every } a.$$

In particular, when $a = -x$,

$$d(x, y) = d(0, y - x) = \| y - x \|$$

The corollary is now obvious.

Proposition 37.5. If $a, b \in \Pi$, and f denotes the translation taking a to b, then writing . and $\circ$ for the inner products in (Π, a) and (Π, b) respectively, we have

$$x.y = f(x) \circ f(y) \quad \textit{for all } x, y \in \Pi$$

Proof. The relation

$$(x + y)^2 = x^2 + y^2 + 2x.y$$

shows that $x.y$ can be expressed in terms of squares of scalars and, therefore, distances. However, f preserves distances and so

$$x.x = f(x) \circ f(x); \quad y.y = f(y) \circ f(y); \quad (x + y).(x + y) = f(x + y) \circ f(x + y)$$

The proposition quickly follows.

Props 22.1 and 37.5 combined show that the translation f is an isomorphism from the inner product space (Π, a) onto the inner product space (Π, b).

38. AN INNER PRODUCT ON THE VECTOR SPACE OF TRANSLATIONS

In No. 23, the set of free vectors (or translations) of Π is turned into a vector space in such a way that for every $0 \in \Pi$, the mapping $x \to \vec{0x}$ is an isomorphism from $(\Pi, 0)$ onto $\mathscr{T}$ (*qua* vector spaces)

For a fixed 0, this mapping evidently defines an induced inner product on $\mathscr{T}$,

which, by Prop. 37.5, is independent of the choice 0 of origin. This fact can be characterized by the property that, for every $0 \in \Pi$,

$$x.y = \vec{0x}.\vec{0y}$$

(the inner products in this equation being evaluated in $(\Pi, 0)$ and $\mathscr{T}$ respectively).

Henceforth then, an expression such as $\vec{ab}.\vec{xy}$ has a clear meaning, and it is often
useful, when one has chosen an origin 0 in Π, to use simultaneously the notations of the
plane $(\Pi, 0)$ and the space $\mathscr{T}$. This is a matter of identifying the two sets by means of
the mapping $x \rightarrow \vec{0x}$.

For example,

$$\vec{xy} = \vec{0y} - \vec{0x} = y - x$$
$$d^2(x,y) = (\vec{xy})^2 = (y - x)^2 = y^2 - 2x.y + x^2$$

Elementary metric properties

39. METRIC RELATIONS IN PARALLELOGRAMS AND TRIANGLES

Proposition 39.1. (a) *In any parallelogram, the sum of the squares of the diagonals is equal to the
sum of the squares of the sides.*

(b) *A parallelogram is a rectangle if and only if its diagonals are equal.*

Proof. To simplify the calculation, take one of the vertices as origin 0. The parallelogram is then of the form $(0, x, x + y, y)$.

The identity $(x + y)^2 + (x - y)^2 = 2(x^2 + y^2)$ gives the first property.
The identity $(x + y)^2 - (x - y)^2 = 4x.y$ shows that

$$(\| x + y \| = \| x - y \|) \Leftrightarrow (x.y = 0) \Leftrightarrow ((0, x, x + y, y) \text{ is a rectangle})$$

*Proposition 39.2. Let (a, b, c) be an arbitrary triangle in Π, such that $a \neq b$ and $a \neq c$. Let
α, β, γ be its sides, and k be the projection ratio of the half-lines $D(a, b)$, $D(a, c)$.*

Then

$$\alpha^2 = \beta^2 + \gamma^2 - 2k\beta\gamma$$

In particular

$$(\alpha^2 = \beta^2 + \gamma^2) \Leftrightarrow (D(a, b) \perp D(a, c))$$

For in (Π, a), we can write:

$$\alpha^2 = d^2(b, c) = (c - b)^2 = c^2 + b^2 - 2c.b = \beta^2 + \gamma^2 - 2k\beta\gamma$$

Again, because $\beta\gamma \neq 0$,

$$(k\beta\gamma = 0) \Leftrightarrow (k = 0) \Leftrightarrow (D(a, b) \perp D(a, c))$$

Here, of course, is the Pythagorean theorem. Another proof will be given in Appendix I
which avoids explicit use of the inner product.

Proposition 39.3. For all $x, y \in (\Pi, 0)$,

$$\| x + y \| \leqslant \| x \| + \| y \|$$

Equality holds only if $x \in [0, y]$ or $y \in [0, x]$.

Proof. The case where $x = 0$ or $y = 0$ is trivial. Suppose therefore that $x \neq 0$ and $y \neq 0$.

Let $\alpha = \| x \|, \beta = \| y \|, \gamma = \| x + y \|$.
Now

$$\gamma^2 = \alpha^2 + \beta^2 + 2\alpha\beta c(x, y) \leqslant \alpha^2 + \beta^2 + 2\alpha\beta = (\alpha + \beta)^2$$

equality holding only when $c(x, y) = 1$.

In other words, $\gamma \leqslant \alpha + \beta$ and equality is realized only when

$$x \in [0, y] \quad \text{or} \quad y \in [0, x]$$

Corollary 39.4. For all $x, y, z \in \Pi$, $d(x, y) \leqslant d(x, z) + d(z, y)$ and equality holds only when $z \in [x, y]$.

For when z is chosen as the origin of Π, the required relation becomes

$$\| x - y \| \leqslant \| x \| + \| y \|$$

and this follows from Prop. 39.3, on changing y to $-y$.

The corollary could be proved just as easily by starting with the relation:

$$\alpha^2 + \beta^2 - 2\alpha\beta c(x, y) \leqslant \alpha^2 + \beta^2 + 2\alpha\beta = (\alpha + \beta)^2$$

which gives equality only when

$$c(x, y) = -1, \quad \text{i.e.} \quad 0 \in [x, y]$$

Proposition 39.5. For every triplet (α, β, γ) of positive numbers, the following statements are equivalent:

(a) *There exists a triangle with sides α, β, γ.*
(b) *The largest of these numbers is at most equal to the sum of the other two.*
(c) *Each of these numbers is at most equal to the sum of the other two.*
(d) *$| \alpha - \beta | \leqslant \gamma \leqslant \alpha + \beta$.*

Proof. We shall prove these equivalences by means of the following chain of implications:

$$a \Rightarrow b \Rightarrow c \Rightarrow d \Rightarrow a$$

1. Corollary 39.4 gives $(a \Rightarrow b)$.

2. $(b \Rightarrow c)$ is clear because if, for example, α and β are $\leqslant \gamma$, then $\alpha \leqslant \beta + \gamma$ and $\beta \leqslant \gamma + \alpha$.

3. $(c \Rightarrow d)$ holds because the inequalities $\alpha \leqslant \beta + \gamma$ and $\beta \leqslant \gamma + \alpha$ can be written as $\alpha - \beta \leqslant \gamma$ and $\beta - \alpha \leqslant \gamma$, showing that $| \alpha - \beta | \leqslant \gamma$, while the relation $\gamma \leqslant \alpha + \beta$ holds by hypothesis.

4. $(d \Rightarrow a)$ is evident if either α or β is zero; suppose therefore that $a \neq 0$ and $\beta \neq 0$.

The relation $|\alpha - \beta| \leqslant \gamma \leqslant \alpha + \beta$ can be rewritten as

$$\alpha^2 + \beta^2 - 2\alpha\beta \leqslant \gamma^2 \leqslant \alpha^2 + \beta^2 + 2\alpha\beta$$

or

$$\gamma^2 = \alpha^2 + \beta^2 - 2k\alpha\beta, \quad \text{where } -1 \leqslant k \leqslant 1$$

Let us assume for the moment that there exists a pair (A, B) of half-lines with origin 0 and such that $c(\mathrm{A}, \mathrm{B}) = k$.

Let x be the point of A such that $d(0, x) = \alpha$, and y be the point of B such that $d(0, y) = \beta$.

The relation

$$d(x, y) = \alpha^2 + \beta^2 - 2\alpha\beta c(\mathrm{A}, \mathrm{B}) = \alpha^2 + \beta^2 - 2k\alpha\beta$$

then shows that the triangle $(0, x, y)$ has sides α, β, γ.

It remains to show that the pair (A, B) exists.

Lemma 39.6. For every number $k \in [-1, 1]$, there exists a pair (A, B) of half-lines with origin 0 and such that $c(\mathrm{A}, \mathrm{B}) = k$.

Proof. Let U, V be two orientated perpendicular lines passing through 0 and let b be the point with coordinates $(k, \sqrt{1 - k^2})$ in the system of axes (U, V). The required half-lines A, B are respectively the positive half-line of U and the half-line D(0, b).

Comment. Notice that the existence of the square root $\sqrt{1 - k^2}$ is critical in the above construction. If the field R is replaced by a suitable subfield K, the lemma is false even though the plane still satisfies Axioms I, II, III, IV.

For example, take K as a subfield of R satisfying

    (i) $x \in \mathrm{K}, y \in \mathrm{K} \Rightarrow (\sqrt{x^2 + y^2} \in \mathrm{K})$

    (ii) $\exists\, a \in \mathrm{K}, a > 0,$ such that $\sqrt{a} \notin \mathrm{K}$

Now, fairly obviously, K^2 has the structure of a plane satisfying Axioms I, II, III, IV. However, the preceding lemma is false in this plane because when $k = (1 - a)/(1 + a)$, $\sqrt{1 - k^2} \notin \mathrm{K}$.

Such fields K can certainly be shown to exist.

It is absolutely essential that pupils should realize that this proof requires the existence of square roots of positive numbers. Failure to do this only leads to complications later. When we investigate the points of intersection of two circles in a subsequent chapter, we shall want to be spared meaningless "pseudo-proofs" based on muddled ideas of continuity.

40. ORTHOGONAL PROJECTION

Proposition 40.1. Let D be a line, $a \in \Pi$, and let p be the orthogonal projection of a onto D. Then

1. *For all $x, y \in \mathrm{D}$,*

$$(d(p, x) = d(p, y)) \Leftrightarrow (d(a, x) = d(a, y))$$

2. *If D_1 is one of the half-lines of D originating at p, the map $x \rightarrow d(a, x)$ from D_1 into R is strictly monotone increasing.*

Proof. These two statements follow immediately from the relation

$$d^2(a, x) = d^2(a, p) + d^2(p, x)$$

We may also add that when it is known that every positive number has a square root, the function $x \rightarrow d(a, x)$ maps D_1 bijectively onto $[d(a, p), \infty)$.

Corollary 40.2. The distance $d(a, x)$ is a minimum if and only if x is the point p.

Corollary 40.3. Let D be a line, $a \notin D$ and $b \in D$. Then

$$(D \perp \Delta(a, b)) \Leftrightarrow (d(a, b) \leqslant d(a, x) \text{ for every } x \in D)$$

Corollary 40.4. If $a, b, c \in \Pi$, and $x \in [b, c]$,

$$d(a, x) \leqslant \sup (d(a, b), d(a, c))$$

Proposition 40.5. Orthogonal projection onto a line diminishes distances.

Proof. Let D be a line and let $x, y \in \Pi$.

Let D' denote the parallel to D passing through x, let x', y' denote the projections of x, y on D, and y'' the projection of y on D'.

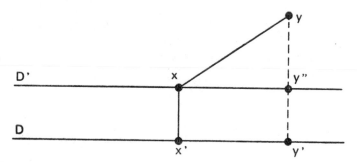

In the rectangle (x, y'', y', x'), $d(x', y') = d(x, y'')$.
In the right-angle triangle (x, y, y''), $d(x, y'') \leqslant d(x, y)$.
Hence, $d(x', y') \leqslant d(x, y)$; and the equality holds only when x, y are on a parallel to D.

41. PERPENDICULAR BISECTOR

Definition 41.1. If $a, b \in \Pi$, and $a \neq b$, the line passing through the mid-point of (a, b), perpendicular to $\Delta(a, b)$, is called the perpendicular bisector *of the pair (a, b).*

Proposition 41.2. Let $a, b \in \Pi$ be such that $a \neq b$. Let 0 be the mid-point of (a, b), and let D be the perpendicular bisector of (a, b).

Then, for every $x \in \Pi$, $d^2(x, b) - d^2(x, a) = 4l\xi$, where $l = d(0, a)$ and where ξ denotes the abscissa of x (on $\Delta(a, b)$ oriented in such a way that $0 < a$) in the system of axes $(\Delta(a, b), D)$.

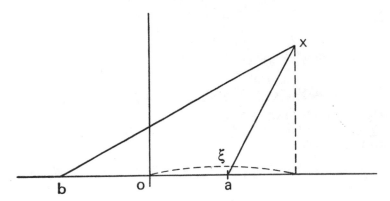

Proof. In the plane $(\Pi, 0)$,

$$d^2(x, b) - d^2(x, a) = (x - b)^2 - (x - a)^2 = (x + a)^2 - (x - a)^2$$
$$= 4a.x = 4l\xi$$

Corollary 41.3. Let D *be the perpendicular bisector of* (a, b) *and let* Π_a, Π_b *be the open half-planes associated with* D *containing* a, b *respectively.*

Then, depending on whether x *is in* Π_b, D, Π_a, *we have:*

$$d(x, b) < d(x, a); \qquad d(x, a) = d(x, b); \qquad d(x, b) > d(x, a)$$

For depending on whether x is in Π_b, D, Π_a,

$$\xi < 0; \qquad \xi = 0; \qquad \xi > 0$$

Thus Proposition 41.2 gives the result.

Corollary 41.4. For every $h \in R$, *the set of points* x *of* Π *such that*

$$d^2(x, b) - d^2(x, a) = h$$

is the line perpendicular to $\Delta(a, b)$ *which meets* $\Delta(a, b)$ *at the point with abscissa* $\xi = h/4l$.

42. MOMENTS OF INERTIA

Definition 42.1. Any finite family of pairs (a_i, α_i), *where* $a_i \in \Pi$ *and* $\alpha_i \in R$, *is called a* system of point masses *of* Π.

For $x \in \Pi$, *the number* $f(x) = \sum_i \alpha_i d^2(x, a_i)$ *is called the* moment of inertia *of this system with respect to* x.

Proposition 42.2. Let $(a_i, \alpha_i)_{i \in I}$ *be a system of point masses of* Π.

1. *When* $\sum \alpha_i = 0$ *the moment of inertia* f *of the system is an affine function of the point* x; *more precisely, in* $(\Pi, 0)$,

$$f(x) = \sum \alpha_i a_i^2 - 2(\sum \alpha_i a_i).x$$

It is therefore constant whenever $\sum \alpha_i a_i = 0$.

2. *When* $\sum \alpha_i \neq 0$,

$$f(x) = (\sum \alpha_i)d^2(a, x) + \sum \alpha_i d^2(a, a_i)$$

where a is the barycentre of the system.

Proof. As

$$f(x) = \sum \alpha_i(x - a_i)^2 = (\sum \alpha_i)x^2 - 2(\sum \alpha_i a_i) \cdot x + \sum \alpha_i a_i^2$$

the first relation must hold when $\sum \alpha_i = 0$.

    When $\sum \alpha_i \neq 0$, we know that $\sum \alpha_i a_i = 0$ when a is taken as origin, and this then gives the required result.

Corollary 42.3. 1. When $\sum \alpha_i = 0$ *and* $\sum \alpha_i a_i \neq 0$, *the set of x such that* $f(x) = h$ *is a line perpendicular to* $\sum \alpha_i a_i$.

2. *When* $\sum \alpha_i \neq 0$, $f(x)$ *has a true minimum or a true maximum at the barycentre a, depending on whether* $\sum \alpha_i$ *is positive or negative. The set of x such that* $f(x) = h$ *is either a circle with centre a, or just* $\{a\}$, *or* $\varnothing$.

Particular cases. When the system is composed of points a, b with masses 1, 1 or 1, -1, we obtain previous results (see Props. 39.1 and 41.2).

43. INNER PRODUCT AND DISTANCE WITH RESPECT TO AN ARBITRARY BASIS

    Let (a_1, a_2) be a basis of the plane Π with origin chosen at 0.

    Let (ξ_1, ξ_2), (ξ_1, ξ_2) be the coordinates of the vectors x, x' with respect to this basis. From

$$x = \xi_1 a_1 + \xi_2 a_2 \quad \text{and} \quad x' = \xi_1' a_1 + \xi_2' a_2$$

we deduce that

$$x \cdot x' = \xi_1 \xi_1' a_1^2 + \xi_2 \xi_2' a_2^2 + (\xi_1 \xi_2' + \xi_1' \xi_2)a_1 \cdot a_2$$

    For $x = x'$, we obtain the quadratic form which expresses $\| x \|^2$ as a function of ξ_1, ξ_2.

    The formulas are greatly simplified if (a_1, a_2) is *an orthonormal basis*, i.e. such that

$$\| a_1 \| = \| a_2 \| = 1 \quad \text{and} \quad a_1 \perp a_2$$

In this case,

$$x \cdot y = \xi_1 \xi_1' + \xi_2 \xi_2' \quad \text{and} \quad \| x \|^2 = \xi_1^2 + \xi_2^2 = x \cdot x$$

Isometries. Similarity transformations. Symmetries of a set

Isometries

In the metric geometry of the plane, the most important transformations are those which simultaneously preserve the affine and metric structure. Among these, the axial symmetries play a special role. We shall see in Appendix I, that it is quite possible to build an axiomatization of the plane which is based on axial symmetries. Not only do they meet the mathematical requirement of generating the group of isometries, they have the added attraction of being the formalization of very simple, everyday processes; bending a piece of paper, turning a plane lamina about a line segment, reflecting in a mirror, etc.

44. Axial symmetries and central symmetries

The oblique symmetry with axis D parallel to a direction δ was introduced in Chapter II. We shall now study the particular case where δ is perpendicular to D, redefining such a symmetry in terms of the notion of perpendicular bisector.

Definition 44.1. If D is a line in Π, symmetry with respect to D (or with axis D) is the mapping f from Π into Π defined as follows:

If $x \in D$, $f(x) = x$.

If $x \notin D$, $f(x)$ is the unique point of Π such that D is the perpendicular bisector of $(x, f(x))$.

It is sometimes convenient to denote the symmetry whose axis is D by (D).
As with an arbitrary oblique symmetry, $f^2 =$ identity, and f is therefore an involution of Π.

Proposition 44.2. Every axial symmetry is an affine transformation of Π. Furthermore, it is an isometry.

Proof. The first property is a special case of Prop. 29.2. Now, let A be the axis of the symmetry f, and B be a perpendicular to A. Taking (A, B) as a system of axes, we see

that if x has components (x_1, x_2) the point $f(x)$ has components $(x_1, -x_2)$. Thus, for all $x, y \in \Pi$, we have

$$(f(x) - f(y))^2 = (x_1 - y_1)^2 + (x_2 - y_2)^2 = (x - y)^2$$

showing that f is indeed an isometry.

Corollary 44.3. An axial symmetry transforms half-lines into half-lines, intervals into intervals (and therefore convex sets into convex sets).

This comes either from the affine nature of the symmetry, or from preservation of distances. It can also be deduced easily from the relation

$$(x_1, x_2) \rightarrow (x_1, -x_2)$$

Corollary 44.4. Every axial symmetry transforms pairs of perpendicular lines into pairs of perpendicular lines.

For symmetry preserves distances, and the fact that two lines are perpendicular can be characterized in terms of distances (Pythagorean theorem or minimum distances, see Corollary 40.3).

Proposition 44.5. Let A, B be two perpendicular lines passing through 0.
The product of the symmetries with axes A, B is the symmetry with centre 0.
The product of the symmetry with axis A, with the symmetry with centre 0, is the symmetry with axis B.

Proof. See Prop. 32.1.

Corollary. Every central symmetry is an isometry.

Proposition 44.6. The product of two symmetries with parallel axes is a translation perpendicular to these axes.
The product of a symmetry with axis D with a translation perpendicular to D is a symmetry with axis parallel to D.

Proof. Let A, B be two parallel lines, and let (D_1, D_2) be a system of axes with $D_1 \parallel A$.

The symmetry with axis A takes the form $(x_1, x_2) \rightarrow (x_1, 2a_2 - x_2)$, and similarly for B.

Hence, the product (B) ∘ (A) of these symmetries becomes the translation:

$$(x_1, x_2) \rightarrow (x_1, x_2 + 2(b_2 - a_2)) = (x_1, x_2) + (0, 2(b_2 - a_2))$$

The second part is proved similarly.

Corollary. Every translation is the product of two symmetries whose axes are perpendicular to the translation; the first (or the second) of these axes can be taken as an arbitrary line perpendicular to the translation.

For the relation

$$t \circ \delta_1 = \delta_2 \text{ is equivalent to } t = \delta_2 \circ \delta_1$$

Similarly,

$$\delta_1 \circ t = \delta_2 \text{ is equivalent to } t = \delta_1 \circ \delta_2$$

It is by means of products of axial symmetries that we shall now carry out a general study of isometries.

45. ISOMETRIES

Certain isometries of the plane have already been encountered. Here we examine the notion systematically.

Definition 45.1. Let $X \subset \Pi$, *and let* f *be a mapping of* X *into* Π. *We say that* f *is an isometry of* X *into* Π, *if for all* $x, y \in X$,

$$d(f(x), f(y)) = d(x, y)$$

Clearly, every isometry is injective, the restriction of an isometry of X to a subset Y of X is an isometry of Y, and the composition of two isometries is also an isometry.

Examples of isometries of Π into itself are translations, axial symmetries and central symmetries.

We now prove a sequence of four propositions leading to an important theorem.

Proposition 45.2. For every $X \subset \Pi$, *any isometry* f *of* X *into* Π *which has at least three non-collinear fixed points, is the identity.*

Proof. Let a_1, a_2, a_3 be fixed points. For all $x \in X$, it follows that

$$d(x, a_i) = d(f(x), f(a_i)) = d(f(x), a_i) \quad (i = 1, 2, 3)$$

Consequently, we cannot have $f(x) \neq x$, for otherwise, the perpendicular bisector of $(x, f(x))$ would contain each a_i, contrary to hypothesis.

Proposition 45.3. For every $X \subset \Pi$, *an isometry* f *of* X *into* Π *which has at least two fixed points* a_1, a_2 *is either the identity or the symmetry whose axis is* $\Delta(a_1, a_2)$.

For, if f is not the identity, there is $a_3 \in X$ such that $a_3 \neq f(a_3)$. The perpendicular bisector of $(a_3, f(a_3))$ contains a_1 and a_2 (the same reasoning as in Prop. 45.2), and therefore is $\Delta(a_1, a_2)$.

This shows that a_1, a_2, a_3 are not collinear, and, letting s_3 denote the symmetry with axis $\Delta(a_1, a_2)$, we see that a_1, a_2, a_3 are all fixed under $s_3 \circ f$. By Prop. 45.2,

$$s_3 \circ f = \text{identity}, \quad \text{giving} \quad f = s_3$$

Corollary. Let A *be an open or closed half-line. An isometry* f *of* Π *into itself with* $f(A) = A$ *is either the identity or the symmetry about the line containing* A.

Proposition 45.4. For every $X \subset \Pi$, *an isometry* f *of* X *into* Π *which has at least one fixed point* a_1 *is either the identity, or an axial symmetry whose axis contains* a_1, *or the product of two such symmetries.*

Proof. If f is not the identity, there exists $a_2 \in X$ such that $a_2 \neq f(a_2)$. The perpendicular bisector D_2 of $(a_2, f(a_2))$ contains a_1, so if s_2 denotes the symmetry whose axis is D_2, a_1 and a_2 are fixed points under $s_2 \circ f$. By Proposition 45.3, we have:

$$s_2 \circ f = \text{identity} \quad \text{or} \quad s_2 \circ f = s_3$$

Thus,

$$f = s_2 \quad \text{or} \quad f = s_2 \circ s_3$$

Proposition 45.5. For all $X \subset \Pi$, *every isometry of* X *into* Π *is the product of at most three axial symmetries* (0, 1, 2, *or* 3).

Proof. If f is not the identity, there exists $a_1 \in X$ such that $a_1 \neq f(a_1)$. If s_1 denotes the symmetry about the perpendicular bisector D_1 of $(a_1, f(a_1))$, a_1 is a fixed point of $s_1 \circ f$.

By Prop. 45.4, it follows that, with the preceding notation,

$$s_1 \circ f = \text{identity} \quad \text{or} \quad s_1 \circ f = s_2 \quad \text{or} \quad s_1 \circ f = s_2 \circ s_3$$

Thus

$$f = s_1 \quad \text{or} \quad f = s_1 \circ s_2 \quad \text{or} \quad f = s_1 \circ s_2 \circ s_3$$

Theorem 45.6. 1. *An isometry of* Π *into itself is either the identity, or has one of the forms* $s_1, s_1 \circ s_2, s_1 \circ s_2 \circ s_3$ *where the s_i are axial symmetries. It is an affine transformation of* Π *and it preserves perpendicularity.*

2. *If* X *is a subset of* Π *and f an isometry from* X *into* Π, f *can be extended to an isometry g of* Π. *If* X *is not collinear the extension g is unique. If* X *is collinear but has two or more points, the extension g can be carried out in just two ways.*

Proof. The first part comes from Prop. 45.5 and the fact that an axial symmetry is an affine transformation of Π which preserves perpendicularity.

For the second part, the existence of g comes from Prop. 45.5.

If g, g' are two extensions of f, $g^{-1} \circ g'$ is the identity on X. If X is not collinear, $g^{-1} \circ g'$ is then the identity on Π, and if X is collinear, but with two or more points, $g^{-1} \circ g'$ is either the identity or the axial symmetry σ whose axis is the line containing X. In the latter case, it follows that either $g' = g$ or $g' = g \circ \sigma$. In any case, the result is proved.

46. GROUP OF ISOMETRIES ABOUT A POINT

The set $\mathscr{I}_0$ of isometries of Π which fix a point 0 is prominent because of the importance of rotations and because it is fundamental for defining angles. In the investigation of such isometries, the axial symmetry is again the basic tool.

It is quite clear that $\mathscr{I}_0$ is a group. We let $\mathscr{S}_0$ be the subset of $\mathscr{I}_0$ consisting of the axial symmetries whose axes pass through 0 and $\mathscr{R}_0$ be the subset consisting of *rotations* about 0, i.e. the set of elements of $\mathscr{I}_0$ of the form $s_1 \circ s_2$, where s_1 and $s_2 \in \mathscr{S}_0$ (in symbols,[1] $\mathscr{R}_0 = \mathscr{S}_0 \circ \mathscr{S}_0$).

Before looking at $\mathscr{I}_0$, $\mathscr{S}_0$ and $\mathscr{R}_0$, we need one more set. This can be taken as either the set of half-lines whose origin is 0 or the injective image of this set on a circle with centre 0.

Thus, let C_0 be the set of points x such that $d(0, x) = 1$ (the lines themselves do not matter very much).

We now compile a list of the properties that we know and which will be the *only* ones required for this topic:

The set C_0 is a subset of the set Π, $\mathscr{I}_0$ is a group of transformations of Π, $\mathscr{S}_0$ is a subset of $\mathscr{I}_0$, and $\mathscr{R}_0$ is defined as $\mathscr{S}_0 \circ \mathscr{S}_0$. The elements of $\mathscr{S}_0$ are called symmetries while those of $\mathscr{R}_0$ are called rotations. Furthermore:

---

1 This notation is quite general in that if A, B are any two subsets of a set E possessing an internal composition τ, we write A τ B for the set $x \tau y$ where $x \in A$ and $y \in B$.

1. For every symmetry σ, $\sigma^2 = $ identity.

2. The identity is not a symmetry.

3. For all $x, y \in C_0$, there is a unique symmetry σ such that $\sigma(x) = y$; denote this by σ_{yx}.

4. For every symmetry σ, there is at least one point x of C_0 such that $\sigma(x) = x$.

5. For every $f \in \mathscr{I}_0$ and every $x \in C_0$

$$(f(x) = x) \Leftrightarrow (f = \text{identity} \quad \text{or} \quad f = \sigma_{xx})$$

All these statements are translations of proved properties:

— In (3), if $y = x$, σ_{xx} is the symmetry whose axis is $\Delta(0, x)$, and if $y \neq x$, σ_{yx} is the symmetry whose axis is the perpendicular bisector of (x, y).

— In (4), the point x of C_0 in question is one of the two points on the axis of σ such that $d(0, x) = 1$.

— Statement (5) is simply a restatement of Prop. 45.3.

Proposition 46.1. No rotation can be a symmetry (i.e. $\mathscr{R}_0 \cap \mathscr{I}_0 = \varnothing$).

Proof. Let $\rho, \sigma, \tau \in \mathscr{I}_0$. By (4), there is $a \in C_0$ with $\tau(a) = a$.

Now,

$$(\rho = \sigma \circ \tau) \Rightarrow (\rho(a) = \sigma(\tau(a)) = \sigma(a))$$

and, by (3),

$$(\rho(a) = \sigma(a)) \Rightarrow (\rho = \sigma)$$

Thus

$$(\rho = \sigma \circ \tau) \Rightarrow (\rho = \sigma)$$

which, in turn, implies that τ is the identity. Hence $\rho = \sigma \circ \tau$ is impossible, and this proves the result.

Proposition 46.2. For all $x, y \in C_0$, there are just two mappings $f \in \mathscr{I}_0$ such that $y = f(x)$; namely, the symmetry σ_{yx} and the rotation $\sigma_{yx} \circ \sigma_{xx}$

Proof.

$$(f(x) = y \quad \text{and} \quad \sigma_{xy} = x) \Rightarrow (\sigma_{xy} \circ f(x) = x)$$

By (5) therefore,

$$\sigma_{xy} \circ f = \text{identity} \quad \text{or} \quad \sigma_{xx}$$

Hence,

$$f = \sigma_{yx} \quad \text{or} \quad f = \sigma_{yx} \circ \sigma_{xx}$$

Corollary 46.3. For all $x, y \in C_0$, there is a unique rotation taking x into y.

Corollary 46.4. $\mathscr{R}_0$ and $\mathscr{I}_0$ partition $\mathscr{I}_0$.

For Prop. 46.2 shows that if $f \in \mathscr{I}_0$ and $a \in C_0$, f must be either the symmetry or the rotation which maps a to $f(a)$.

Proposition 46.5. If $f \in \mathscr{R}_0$ and $\sigma \in \mathscr{I}_0$, there is a $\tau \in \mathscr{I}_0$ such that $f = \tau \circ \sigma$ (and a τ' such that $f = \sigma \circ \tau'$).

Proof. By (4), we can find $a \in C_0$ such that $\sigma(a) = a$.

Put $f(a) = b$.

Now $\sigma_{ba} \circ \sigma(a) = b$, and so, by Corollary 46.3, the rotations f and $\sigma_{ba} \circ \sigma$ are the same.

Hence τ is simply the symmetry σ_{ba}.

As the inverse of any rotation is a rotation, this also shows that there is $\tau' \in \mathcal{S}_0$ such that

$$f^{-1} = \tau' \circ \sigma \quad \text{and} \quad f = \sigma \circ \tau'$$

Proposition 46.6. Products involving an even (resp. odd) number of symmetries are always rotations (resp. symmetries).

Proof. By using induction on the number of factors, it is sufficient to show that the product of three symmetries is always a symmetry. However, by Prop. 46.5, if $\pi, \rho, \sigma \in \mathcal{S}_0$, there is $\tau \in \mathcal{S}_0$ such that $\pi \circ \rho = \tau \circ \sigma$. Thus, $\pi \circ \rho \circ \sigma = \tau$ and the result is proved.

Theorem 46.7. 1. *The set $\mathcal{R}_0$ is an abelian subgroup of $\mathcal{I}_0$.*

2. *For every $\sigma \in \mathcal{S}_0$, $\sigma \circ \mathcal{R}_0 = \mathcal{R}_0 \circ \sigma = \mathcal{S}_0$.*

3. *The group $\mathcal{R}_0$ is simply transitive[2] on C_0.*

Proof. 1. By Prop. 46.6, the product of two rotations is another rotation. The inverse of the rotation $\rho \circ \sigma$ is $\sigma \circ \rho$, which is also a rotation. Thus $\mathcal{R}_0$ is a group, and we must show that it is abelian.

For every $f, g \in \mathcal{R}_0$ and every $\sigma \in \mathcal{S}_0$, we can find $\pi, \rho \in \mathcal{S}_0$ such that $f = \pi \circ \sigma$ and $g = \sigma \circ \rho$. It follows that:

$$(f \circ g = g \circ f) \Leftrightarrow (\pi \circ \sigma \circ \sigma \circ \rho = \sigma \circ \rho \circ \pi \circ \sigma) \Leftrightarrow ((\pi \circ \rho \circ \sigma)^2 = \text{identity})$$

However, as $\pi \circ \rho \circ \sigma$ is a symmetry, this last equality does hold by Prop. 46.6. Hence, $f \circ g = g \circ f$.

2. By Prop. 46.6, $\sigma \circ \mathcal{R}_0 \subseteq \mathcal{S}_0$, and $\sigma \circ \mathcal{S}_0 \subseteq \mathcal{R}_0$.

This last inclusion gives $\mathcal{S}_0 \subseteq \sigma \circ \mathcal{R}_0$, i.e. $\sigma \circ \mathcal{R}_0 = \mathcal{S}_0$.

Similarly, $\mathcal{R}_0 \circ \sigma = \mathcal{S}_0$.

This shows, in fact, that $\mathcal{R}_0$ is a normal subgroup of $\mathcal{I}_0$, and that any coset of $\mathcal{R}_0$ containing an element f of $\mathcal{I}_0$ is either $\mathcal{R}_0$ or $\mathcal{S}_0$ depending on whether $f \in \mathcal{R}_0$ or $f \in \mathcal{S}_0$. The factor group $\mathcal{I}_0 / \mathcal{R}_0$ is of order 2.

3. The third property is true by Corollary 46.3.

We shall have more to say about rotations when we have defined angles. For the moment, we shall use the results that we have obtained to make a brief examination of the isometries of Π.

47. EVEN AND ODD ISOMETRIES

Definition 47.1. An isometry of Π is called even (resp. odd)[3] *if it is the product of an even (resp. odd) number of axial symmetries.*

---

2 That is, for all $x, y \in C_0$, there exists a unique $f \in \mathcal{R}_0$ such that $y = f(x)$.

3 The terminology "even", "odd" reminds us of the definition. "Direct" and "inverse" was rejected because of possible confusion between the terms "inverse isometry" and "inverse of an isometry". Again, "positive, negative" was rejected to avoid the situation of having a central symmetry which

In what follows, we shall let $\mathscr{I}$, $\mathscr{I}^+$, $\mathscr{I}^-$ respectively denote the set of isometries, the set of even isometries, and the set of odd isometries of Π.

By Theorem 45.6, $\mathscr{I} = \mathscr{I}^+ \cup \mathscr{I}^-$, and we shall soon show that $\mathscr{I}^+ \cap \mathscr{I}^- = \varnothing$. It is immediately clear from the definition that $\mathscr{I}^+$ is a subgroup of $\mathscr{I}$, and even a normal subgroup.

Our aim is to reduce the analysis of an arbitrary isometry to that of one about a point 0. The method adopted is easily adaptable to space, and its translation into analytic terms is equally apparent.

The group of translations of Π will be denoted by $\mathscr{T}$. The symbols $\mathscr{I}_0$, $\mathscr{S}_0$, $\mathscr{R}_0$ are as defined in No. 46.

Lemma 47.2. 1. *If* $f \in \mathscr{I}$, *f can be uniquely written in the form* $f = t \circ \bar{f}$, *where* $t \in \mathscr{T}$ *and* $\bar{f} \in \mathscr{I}_0$. *The map* $\bar{f}$ *will be called the reduced form of f in* $(\Pi, 0)$.

2. *If f is a symmetry whose axis is* D, *its reduced form is the symmetry whose axis* D' *passes through* 0 *and is parallel to* D.

Proof. 1. We require f to be expressed in the form $x \to a + \bar{f}(x)$ relative to $(\Pi, 0)$.

Uniqueness: If f is of this form, then clearly

$$a = f(0) \quad \text{and} \quad \bar{f}(x) = f(x) - f(0)$$

Existence: Let $\bar{f}$ be the map $x \to f(x) - f(0)$. It is an isometry and it leaves 0 fixed. Hence $\bar{f} \in \mathscr{I}_0$.

On the other hand, as $f(x) = f(0) + \bar{f}(x)$, this is the required canonical form.

2. Let g be the symmetry whose axis is D'. By Prop. 44.6, $f \circ g$ is a translation t. But $f = t \circ g$ and so $g = \bar{f}$.

Proposition 47.3. 1. *The map* $f \to \bar{f}$ *from* $\mathscr{I}$ *to* $\mathscr{I}_0$ *is a homomorphism.*

2. *The images of* $\mathscr{I}^+$ *and* $\mathscr{I}^-$ *under this mapping are* $\mathscr{R}_0$ *and* $\mathscr{S}_0$ *respectively.*

Proof. 1. Take $f, g \in \mathscr{I}$ and let $\bar{f}$, $\bar{g}$ be their reduced forms.

Now $\bar{f}$ and $\bar{g}$ are linear maps. Thus, from

$$f(x) = f(0) + \bar{f}(x), \quad g(y) = g(0) + \bar{g}(y)$$

we obtain the equations

$$g(f(x)) = g(0) + \bar{g}(f(0)) + \bar{g}(\bar{f}(x)) = g(f(0)) + \bar{g}(\bar{f}(x))$$

Hence $\overline{(g \circ f)} = \bar{g} \circ \bar{f}$, and the mapping is a homomorphism.

2. By Lemma 47.2, the reduced form $\bar{f}$ of the axial symmetry f is also an axial

---

was a positive isometry but had negative proportionality ratio. Finally, "direct, indirect" was rejected because the intuitive meaning behind this notation only becomes clear after a thorough study of the rigid motions of a plane onto itself.

symmetry. What we have just proved shows that the reduced form of a product of n axial symmetries is a product of n elements of $\mathscr{S}_0$. The result is now clear.

Corollary 47.4. The sets $\mathscr{I}^+$ and $\mathscr{I}^-$ constitute a partition of $\mathscr{I}$. For every $\sigma \in \mathscr{I}^-$, $\sigma \mathscr{I}^+ = \mathscr{I}^+ \sigma = \mathscr{I}^-$.

Corollary 47.5. If A_1, A_2 are a pair of closed half-lines of Π, there is a unique even isometry taking A_1 into A_2. Similarly, there is a unique odd isometry with the same property.

This follows from Theorem 45.6 and Corollary 47.4.

An interesting subgroup of $\mathscr{I}^+$

The group of central symmetries and translations of Π is a subgroup of $\mathscr{I}^+$. In fact, every such transformation is the product of two axial symmetries.

48. ANALYSING ISOMETRIES

Let $t \circ \bar{f}$ be the canonical form in $(\Pi, 0)$ of an isometry f.

1. If $\bar{f}$ is a rotation, write t as $\rho \circ \sigma$, where ρ and σ are axial symmetries, the axis of σ passing through 0. We know that we can write $\bar{f}$ as $\sigma \circ \tau$, where τ is another axial symmetry.

Thus,

$$f = t \circ \bar{f} = \rho \circ \sigma \circ \sigma \circ \tau = \rho \circ \tau$$

showing that f is either a translation or a rotation (depending on whether or not ρ, τ have parallel axes).

2. If $\bar{f}$ is an axial symmetry, choose a system of perpendicular axes in which the axis of $\bar{f}$ is the x-axis.

Relative to these, f takes the form

$$(x_1 \ x_2) \rightarrow (x_1 + a_1, -x_2 + a_2)$$

and by a suitable translation of the first axis, this becomes

$$(x_1, x_2) \rightarrow (x_1 + a_1, -x_2)$$

If $a_1 = 0$, f is an axial symmetry. Otherwise, although f globally preserves a line D, it is not the symmetry whose axis is D.

To summarize:

Proposition 48.1. 1. Every even isometry is the product of two axial symmetries. It is either a translation or a rotation.

2. Every odd isometry is the product of an axial symmetry and a translation parallel to the axis of this symmetry.

The fixed points of isometries are easily derived from this result.

Similitudes

49. CHARACTERISTIC PROPERTIES

Definition 49.1. Let $X \subset \Pi$, f a mapping from X into Π, and k a positive number. The map f is called a similitude with proportionality ratio k if, for all $x, y \in X$,

$$d(f(x), f(y)) = kd(x, y)$$

Similitudes with ratio 1 are precisely isometries.

Lemma 49.2. A dilation with proportionality ratio h is a similitude with ratio $|h|$.

For in $(\Pi, 0)$, such a dilation can be written as

$$x \to hx + a$$

Thus

$$d(f(x), f(y)) = \|f(x) - f(y)\| = |h| \, \|x - y\| = |h| \, d(x, y)$$

Proposition 49.3. If $X \subset \Pi$, a similitude f from X into Π with ratio k can be extended to a similitude from Π into itself, with ratio k. This extension is unique if X is not collinear and can be carried out in two ways if X is collinear but contains two or more points.

Proof. If φ is a homothetic transformation of Π with proportionality ratio k, $\varphi^{-1} \circ f$ is an isometry of X. Thus $\varphi^{-1} \circ f$ can be extended to an isometry ψ of Π, uniquely if X is not collinear, in two ways if X is collinear but contains two or more points (Theorem 45.6). The similitude $\varphi \circ \psi$ gives the required extension.

In view of this proposition, we need only study similitudes of Π into itself.

Proposition 49.4. A similitude of Π with ratio k is the product of a homothetic transformation of this ratio and an isometry.

It is an affine transformation and it preserves perpendicularity.

The similitudes of Π are a group S and the map $f \to k(f)$, where $k(f)$ is the ratio, is a homomorphism of S into the multiplicative group R_+^*.

Taken in the indicated order, these results are all proved easily. Here is a converse of one of them.

Proposition 49.5. Any affine transformation of Π preserving perpendicularity is a similitude.

Proof. Let f be the given transformation, and let A_1, A_2 be two perpendicular half-lines originating at 0. Now $f(A_1)$, $f(A_2)$ are two perpendicular half-lines originating at $f(0)$, and thus there is an isometry g taking A_1, A_2 to $f(A_1)$, $f(A_2)$.

The map $g^{-1} \circ f$ is a linear transformation of $(\Pi, 0)$ preserving perpendicularity, sending A_1, A_2 onto themselves. If (a_1, a_2) is the basis of $(\Pi, 0)$ defined by $\|a_i\| = 1$, $a_i \in A_i$ ($i = 1, 2$), then relative to this basis, $g^{-1} \circ f$ is the map

$$(\xi_1, \xi_2) \to (\alpha_1 \xi_1, \alpha_2 \xi_2) \quad \text{where } \alpha_1, \alpha_2 > 0$$

But $(1, 1)$ and $(1, -1)$ are perpendicular and, by expressing the fact that their images are perpendicular, we get

$$\alpha_1^2 - \alpha_2^2 = 0 \quad \text{or} \quad \alpha_1 = \alpha_2$$

Thus, $g^{-1} \circ f$ is the homothetic transformation $H(0, \alpha_1)$ and $f = g \circ H(0, \alpha_1)$. This proves the result.

50. EVEN AND ODD SIMILITUDES

Definition 50.1. A similitude f of Π is said to be even (resp. odd) if it can be written in the form $f = d \circ g$, where d is a dilation of positive ratio, and g is an even (resp. odd) isometry.

Proposition 50.2. No similitude of Π is both even and odd.

Proof. From the relation $d \circ g = \delta \circ \gamma$, we deduce that $\delta^{-1} \circ d = \gamma \circ g^{-1}$. This has the form:

$$(\text{dilation of positive ratio}) = (\text{isometry})$$

which can only hold if both sides are translations; i.e. $\gamma \circ g^{-1}$ is an even isometry. Thus, γ and g must have the same parity.

Theorem 50.3. 1. *The product of two similitudes is even or odd depending on whether or not they have the same parity.*

2. *The set S^+ of even similitudes is a group which operates transitively on the pairs (x, y) of distinct points of Π.*

Proof. 1. Let $f, g \in S$. In the plane $(\Pi, 0)$, taking λ to be the proportionality ratio of f, the similitude $\bar{f}: x \to \frac{1}{\lambda} (f(x) - f(0))$ is an element of $\mathscr{I}_0$ and

$$f(x) = f(0) + \lambda \bar{f}(x)$$

Similarly,

$$g(y) = g(0) + \mu \bar{g}(y) \quad \text{where} \quad \bar{g} \in \mathscr{I}_0$$

As $\bar{g}$ is linear, we have

$$g \circ f(x) = g \circ f(0) + \lambda \mu \bar{g} \circ \bar{f}(x)$$

As the parities of $f, g, g \circ f$ are respectively those of $\bar{f}, \bar{g}, \bar{g} \circ \bar{f}$, the statement now follows.

2. It is now clear that S^+ is a group. The remainder of the proposition follows from Prop. 49.3. For if $X = \{x, y\}$ and $X' = \{x', y'\}$ where $x \neq y$, $x' \neq y'$, this proposition asserts that the map $x \to x'$, $y \to y'$ from X onto X' can be extended to a similitude f of Π in two ways; one giving rise to an even similitude, the other to an odd.

As a consequence, we see that the set $A = (\Pi \times \Pi - $ its diagonal$)$ with an arbitrary point (x_0, y_0) taken as origin can be given a canonical group structure isomorphic to S^+ in which (x_0, y_0) corresponds to the identity. This identification of A with S^+ is useful. For example, it allows us to define a topology on S^+, obtained as the image of the topology of A (considered as a subset of $\Pi \times \Pi$) under this canonical mapping.

Proposition 50.4. A dilation (of positive or negative proportionality ratio) is an even similitude.

For it is a product of translations, positive homothetic transformations and central symmetries, and these are all even similitudes.

51. GROUP OF SIMILITUDES ABOUT A POINT

Proposition 51.1. 1. *The group* S_0 *of similitudes fixing* 0 *is the direct product of the group of positive homothetic transformations centre* 0 *(isomorphic to* R_+^**) and the group* $\mathscr{I}_0$ *of isometries.*

2. *The subgroup of even similitudes* S_0^+ *of* S_0 *is abelian and is simply transitive on* $\Pi^* = \Pi - \{0\}$.

Proof. 1. Let $f, g \in S_0$ and let λ, μ be their proportionality ratios.

Then f and g can be put uniquely in the form

$$f = \lambda \bar{f} \qquad g = \mu \bar{g} \quad \text{where } \bar{f}, \bar{g} \in \mathscr{I}_0$$

Now

$$f \circ g(x) = \lambda \bar{f}(\mu \bar{g}(x)) = \lambda \mu (\bar{f} \circ \bar{g})(x), \quad \text{giving } f \circ g = (\lambda \mu)(\bar{f} \circ \bar{g})$$

This shows that the mapping $f \to (\lambda, \bar{f})$ from S_0 onto the direct product $R_+^* \times \mathscr{I}_0$ is indeed an isomorphism.

2. In particular, S_0^+ is isomorphic to the group $R_+^* \times \mathscr{R}_0$ and, as both factors are abelian, so is S_0^+.

By Theorem 50.3, if $x, x' \in \Pi^*$, there is a unique even similitude f taking $(0, x)$ to $(0, x')$. As $f(0) = 0$, $f \in S_0$, and this completes the proof.

51.2. Applications to the construction of the complex number field.

Choose a point $e \in \Pi^*$.

The second part of Prop. 51.1 shows that the mapping φ from S_0^+ onto Π^* defined by $f \to f(e)$ is one-one.

We transfer the group structure of S_0^+ to Π^* by means of the mapping φ and write the group operation in Π^* multiplicatively. (Thus, products under this operation are images of group compositions in S_0^+.) The operation can be extended to the whole of Π by putting $x0 = 0x = 0$, for every $x \in \Pi$.

Now for every $x, y \in \Pi$, the element of S_0^+ taking e to xy is the product of the elements $f, g \in S_0^+$ taking e to x and y respectively. In other words, $xy = f \circ g(e) = f(y)$; and this is also clearly valid for $y = 0$.

As f is linear, we see then that for all $a, b \in \Pi$:

$$x(a + b) = f(a + b) = f(a) + f(b) = xa + xb$$

It is easily shown that, with the addition of $(\Pi, 0)$ and the multiplication just defined, the elements of Π become a commutative field whose zero is 0 and whose identity is e.

We now have all the elements required for a formal definition of the complex numbers. Let i be one of the two vectors perpendicular to e of norm $\|e\|$, and let f be the rotation which transforms e to i.

The relation $i \perp e$ implies $f(i) \perp f(e)$ where $f(i) \perp i$. Thus,

$$f(i) = e \quad \text{or} \quad f(i) = -e$$

In terms of the group multiplication, this gives

$$i^2 = -e \quad \text{or} \quad i^2 = e$$

However, the second solution implies $(e + i)(e - i) = e - i^2 = 0$, and this is impossible in a field. Hence, $i^2 = -e$.

The vectors e, i form a basis of $(\Pi, 0)$ and every $x \in \Pi$ can be written as

$$x = \alpha e + \beta i \quad \text{where } \alpha, \beta \in R$$

If we identify every $\lambda \in R$ with the point λe of $(\Pi, 0)$, it follows immediately that for every $u \in (\Pi, 0)$, λu is the product of λe with u. We can consequently write

$$x = \alpha e + \beta i = \alpha + \beta i \quad \text{with } \alpha \text{ and } \beta \in (\Pi, 0)$$

Thus,

$$(\alpha + \beta i)(\alpha' + \beta' i) = (\alpha\alpha' - \beta\beta') + i(\alpha\beta' + \alpha'\beta)$$

and it is clear that the field structure that we have defined on Π is isomorphic to the field structure which is defined on R^2 by the operations:

$$(\alpha, \beta) + (\alpha', \beta') = (\alpha + \alpha', \beta + \beta')$$
$$(\alpha, \beta) \times (\alpha', \beta') = ((\alpha\alpha' - \beta\beta'), (\alpha\beta' + \alpha'\beta))$$

Generally speaking, when we talk about the field C of complex numbers we are referring to the plane R^2 and the operations described above. The field structure defined on $(\Pi, 0, e)$ is really just a convenient geometrical model of C.

52. Analysing similitudes

We have already analysed similitudes with ratio $k = 1$; those with ratio $k \neq 1$ are much less varied.

Proposition 52.1. A similitude f of Π, with ratio $k \neq 1$, has a unique fixed point called the centre of f.

The most elegant proof would run as follows. As f and f^{-1} have the same fixed points, there is no loss of generality in assuming that $k < 1$; thus, f is a contraction and, as Π is a complete metric space, f has a unique fixed point given as the limit of the sequence $(f^n(a))$ (a an arbitrary point of Π).

However, the ideas involved in this proof are by no means elementary, and it is based on the fact that R satisfies the axiom of continuity, an axiom not necessary for the development of elementary geometry. For this reason, we shall not use this proof.

Possible proofs based on the notion of angle and arc must be firmly rejected for a different reason: they bring in angles and circles when the matter is essentially one of linear algebra.

The proper solution is to resolve the vector equation

$$f(0) + k\vec{f}(x) = x \quad (\vec{f} \in I_0)$$

in the plane $(\Pi, 0)$ that we have chosen.

1. If $\vec{f} \in \mathscr{S}_0$, taking a set of axes in which the X-axis is the axis of $\vec{f}$, the equation gives

$$kx_1 + a_1 = x_1; \quad -kx_2 + a_2 = x_2$$

from which x_1 and x_2 are easily calculated.

2. If $\bar{f} \in R_0$, then, in terms of the system $(\Pi, 0, e)$ of 51.2, we have

$$f(0) + \alpha z = z \quad \text{where } \alpha \neq e$$

and in this case,

$$z = f(0)/(1 - \alpha)$$

Proposition 52.1 completely determines the structure of the similitudes with proportionality ratio $k \neq 1$. We see that if f is a similitude with centre a and ratio k, then:

If f is even, f is an element of S_a^+.

If f is odd, f is the product of the homothetic transformation $H(a, k)$ and a symmetry whose axis passes through a. This axis is called the *axis of the similitude f*.

53. CLASSIFICATION OF CLOSED GROUPS OF SIMILITUDES

The only groups of affine transformations that are useful in geometry, or even analysis, are those which are *closed* in the natural topology defined [4] on the group of affine transformations by the coefficients of the matrices representing the transformations (with respect to some basis).

A systematic investigation of certain closed subgroups of the similitude group is outlined in the Exercises. Here we shall simply give a classification. Some of these groups make excellent classwork material and, in any case, it is useful to know the closed subgroups of R, R^2 and the multiplicative groups R^*, C^*.

In the additive group R, the closed subgroups are R itself and the discrete groups $\{n\alpha\}_{n \in Z}$, where $\alpha \in R$.

For the additive group R^2, they are the images under injective linear maps from R^2 onto itself of the subgroups:

$$R^2, \quad Z^2, \quad R \times Z, \quad R \times \{0\}, \quad Z \times \{0\}, \quad \{0\} \times \{0\}$$

In C^*, the closed subgroups are the images under $z \to e^z$ from C onto C^* of the closed subgroups of the additive group C (isomorphic to R^2). In particular, the closed subgroups of R^* are:

$$R^*, R_+^* \text{ and each subset } \{k^n\}_{n \in Z} \quad \text{where } k \neq 0$$

53.1. Closed groups of dilations of Π (or more generally of an Euclidean space).

Let $(E, 0)$ be a n-dimensional Euclidean space with origin 0. To simplify the notation, identify the translation $x \to x + a$ of E with the point a of $(E, 0)$. Thus, groups of translations of E become subgroups of $(E, 0)$.

(a) *Translations*. The closed groups of translations of E are the images under a linear mapping from R^n into $(E, 0)$ of the subgroups of R^n of the form

$$R^p \times Z^q \times \{0\}^r \quad \text{where } p + q + r = n$$

---

[4] Relative to a chosen basis in Π, every affine transformation f of Π can be written

$$x' = ax + by + c, \qquad y' = a'x + b'y + c', \quad \text{where } ab' - ba' \neq 0$$

If we identify the set of such f with the set of points (a, b, c, a', b', c') of R^6 for which $ab' - ba' \neq 0$, it is natural to choose the topology on the set induced by that of R^6, and in this way the group $\mathscr{A}$ of affine transformations is topologized. It is easily shown that this topology obtained is independent of the choice of basis, and that the operations $f \to f^{-1}$ and $(f, g) \to f \circ g$ are continuous. A subgroup of $\mathscr{A}$ is called closed if it is a closed subset in this topology of $\mathscr{A}$.

3*

(b) *Central symmetries-translations*. The group generated by central symmetries whose centres are in G, where G is any closed subgroup of (E, 0).

(c) *Other subgroups*. The group of dilations $x \rightarrow kx + a$, where k ranges over a closed subgroup G of R^*, and a ranges over an affine subspace of E (eventually reducible to a single point).

53.2. *Closed groups of isometries of* Π.

(a) Closed groups about a point 0.

These are $\mathscr{I}_0$, $\mathscr{R}_0$ and finite rotation groups (generated by a pair of axial symmetries whose axes are inclined at an angle of $2\pi/n$).

(b) The group generated by a closed subgroup G of $\mathscr{I}_0$ and the translations of Π.

(c) Infinite discrete[5] groups of isometries.

These are arbitrary subgroups of the following groups:

— The group generated by four symmetries whose axes form a rectangle.

— The group generated by three symmetries whose axes form an equilateral triangle (alternatively, a rectangular isosceles triangle).

These subgroups are very varied; as examples, we single out:

— the group generated by an odd isometry;

— the group generated by two rotations of 60° (or 120°) with distinct centres.

In any infinite discrete group of isometries, every rotation has period 2, 3, 4 or 6—a remarkable limitation long known to decorators.

53.3. *Other closed groups of similitudes of* Π.

(a) Groups of even similitudes about a point 0.

If we identify the plane Π* with C*, the groups we are looking for are precisely the closed subgroups of C* listed above.

(b) Groups of arbitrary similitudes about 0. The determination of these is left as an exercise.

(c) Groups generated by closed subgroups G of similitudes about 0 and the translations of Π.

3. Sets stable under a group of transformations

54. REGULARITY IN A SET

The sense of regularity or symmetry given by certain sets can be translated mathematically into the fact that they are invariant under some transformation group. This invariance gives them a certain homogeneity.

---

5 Subgroups of the group of affine transformations which consist of discrete subsets, i.e. having only isolated points.

More exactly, if E is a set and $\mathscr{E}$ a transformation group on E, then providing each transformation preserves something sufficiently tangible, E will give an impression of symmetry. The more elements in $\mathscr{E}$, the stronger the impression; but this is not to say that we can think of E as being more beautiful. Beauty is a subjective notion not translatable into mathematical terms.

For example; suppose we say that the pair (E, $\mathscr{E}$) is a homogeneous space when $\mathscr{E}$ operates transitively on E; i.e. for all $x, y \in$ E, there is $f \in \mathscr{E}$ such that $f(x) = y$. If the elements of $\mathscr{E}$ do not have a character which is sufficiently tangible to an observer, he may well miss the regularity of E. Thus, a homeomorphism (continuous transformation with a continuous inverse) does not really mean much to a non-mathematical observer and, although the set of closed simple curves is homogeneous under the group of homeomorphisms, there is no general impression of regularity.

In other words, a *feeling* of symmetry only appears if the transformations of $\mathscr{E}$ preserve the *shape* of E in some suitable sense: this is why, even though affine transformations are now more familiar than homeomorphisms, they still have a somewhat weak and shaky character. And the pairs (E, $\mathscr{E}$) which are usually called regular or symmetric (for the want of a better word) are those where E is a subset of an Euclidean space, and where the elements of $\mathscr{E}$ are restrictions of isometries or, in exceptional cases, similitudes of the space.

We shall only be interested in the regularity of *sets*. Anything orientated more towards aesthetics, mechanics or physics would also have to take into account the regularity of the colour (with all the nuances of its spectrum), the mass, chemical composition, magnetism, etc.

55. Construction of regular pairs (E, $\mathscr{E}$)

We aim to give a systematic method for constructing regular pairs (E, $\mathscr{E}$) which is valid for both the plane and space.

Let A be a set having a group of transformations $\mathscr{A}$.

For every $X \subset A$ and every $f \in \mathscr{A}$, $f(X) \subset f(A) = A$.

Set $\mathscr{A}(X) = E = \bigcup_{f \in \mathscr{A}} f(X)$

Then, if $g \in \mathscr{A}$,

$$g(E) = g\left(\bigcup_f f(X)\right) = \bigcup_f g \circ f(X)$$

However, as $\mathscr{A}$ is a group, $g \circ f$ ranges over $\mathscr{A}$ as f ranges over $\mathscr{A}$, and this implies that $g(E) = E$, for every $g \in \mathscr{A}$.

If we let $\mathscr{E}$ be the set of transformations obtained by restricting the elements of $\mathscr{A}$ to E, $\mathscr{E}$ is a group of transformations of E (although, of course, it could well happen that E is preserved by interesting transformations other than those in $\mathscr{E}$).

We say that (E, $\mathscr{E}$) is *generated* by X in (A, $\mathscr{A}$). Borrowing from the decorative arts, we might even say that X is the *motif* which generates E.

The mapping from $f \in \mathscr{A}$ to its restriction to E is a homomorphism from $\mathscr{A}$ onto $\mathscr{E}$; it need not be injective.

The simplest motifs are those consisting of but one point. For $x \in A$, let us define the

orbit of x as the set $E = \mathscr{A}(\{x\})$. The *orbits* are then the classes of the equivalence relation on A defined by $(x \sim y)$ if there exists $f \in \mathscr{A}$ such that $f(x) = y$.

Various orbits of $\mathscr{A}$ can have different structures. For example, if $\mathscr{A}$ is the group of transformations of a plane A generated by two symmetries with perpendicular axes, orbits can contain one, two or four points.

The relation $\mathscr{A}\left(\bigcup X_i\right) = \bigcup_i \mathscr{A}(X_i)$ shows that the sets $\mathscr{A}(X)$ are precisely those sets which are the union of orbits. Thus, the sets E are known once the orbits of A are known.

The case of Euclidean spaces

When A is a plane (or more generally an Euclidean space), and $\mathscr{A}$ is a group of similitudes, we are usually only interested in the case where $\mathscr{A}$ is a closed group, and the subset E in the pair (E, $\mathscr{E}$) is closed.

The classification of closed groups of similitudes given above simplifies the finding of sets E stable under such groups. In fact, they are the unions of orbits, and for each of the groups that we have listed, these orbits are easily determined.

Notice that many of the groups give rise to rather dull sets E; for example, it can happen that every orbit is the whole space. In contrast to this, infinite discrete groups of isometries and groups of even similitudes about a point provide sets which are both charming and decorative.

56. Symmetries of a given set

We have seen how we can construct the sets E which are stable under a given group $\mathscr{A}$ of similitudes of Π. We have pointed out already that such a set can be stabilized by similitudes outside $\mathscr{A}$. This suggests the more general problem of determining for a given set E, of Π, the set of similitudes f such that $f(E) = E$. Whatever the answer, this set is clearly some group $\mathscr{G}$.

In elementary geometry, it has become a custom to be interested only in those elements of $\mathscr{G}$ which are axial or central symmetries. In general, as these do not form a group, this means that an excellent opportunity for studying a group of transformations is lost and we debar ourselves from forming the products of the symmetries that we obtain. What is more, by limiting ourselves to the symmetries, we overlook the important roles played by the translations and homothetic transformations. To take an example, the cones in R^n with vertex 0 are best defined as sets stabilized by the group of positive homothetic transformations centred at 0; and cylinders with direction δ are sets which are stable under the group of translations parallel to δ.

Nevertheless, the role played by the axes and centres of symmetries is fundamental, and it is vital that pupils should readily recognize the symmetries of the following simple sets:

— Line, half-line, interval, set of two points.
— Union of two lines (intersecting, perpendicular or otherwise, parallel).
— Union of two half-lines with same origin.
— Isosceles triangle, equilateral triangle, rectangle.

Later, we shall be examining the symmetries of a pair of circles, and the symmetries of the configuration consisting of a circle and a line.

Two simple principles should be borne in mind when searching for symmetries (axial or central):

1. If A and B are stable under a symmetry φ, so are $A \cup B$, $A \cap B$ and the complements of A, B.

2. For every subset X, $X \cap \varphi(X)$ and $X \cup \varphi(X)$ are stable under φ.

The following is also very useful:

3. Let (D_i) be a finite family of distinct lines. Then every line in $\bigcup D_i$ is one of the lines D_i.

This must be true because any line has an infinity of points and by the "Pigeon-hole" principle it must meet some D_i in two or more points, i.e. it is D_i.

Analogous results clearly hold for families of circles or families of lines and circles. Assuming that the cardinal of the continuum is uncountable and greater than the cardinal of any countable set, they can be extended to countable families.

We shall consider just one simple example.

Example. Suppose we assume that the only axes of symmetry for a line D are the lines perpendicular to D and D itself. Let us determine the axes of symmetry for the configuration consisting of a pair of distinct parallel lines A, B.

The axes common to A and B are the perpendiculars to A and B. On the other hand, as A, B are symmetric with respect to the parallel D to A, B equidistant from these two lines, the line D is also an axis of symmetry of $A \cup B$.

It remains to show that $A \cup B$ has no axis other than these.

Suppose φ is a symmetry with axis C such that $\varphi(A \cup B) = A \cup B$.

Then, $\varphi(A) \subset A \cup B$ and by property 3 listed above, the line $\varphi(A)$ is either A or B. If $\varphi(A) = A$, C is an axis of A and, as the solution $C = A$ is immediately eliminated, we see that C is perpendicular to A. If $\varphi(A) = B$, it immediately follows that C meets neither A nor B. Hence C is parallel to A and B and equidistant from these lines. It is, therefore, the axis D that we have already found.

Exercises on Chapter IV

1. Let A, B be two lines of Π. For every $x \in \Pi$, let $\alpha(x)$ and $\beta(x)$ denote the distances from x to A and B respectively, and let $f(x) = \alpha(x) + \beta(x)$. Describe the set of x such that $f(x) \leqslant l$ (or $f(x) = l$), where l is a given positive number.

For a given arbitrary line D, determine the points x of D for which $f(x)$ is a minimum. What is the condition for there to be a unique such x?

2. Let (D_i) be a finite family of lines and, for every $x \in \Pi$, let $\alpha_i(x)$ be the distance of x from D_i. Show that each of the functions α_i is convex.

Hence, deduce that the set of x such that $\sum \lambda_i \alpha_i(x) \leqslant l$ (where each λ_i and l are non-negative numbers) is a convex polygon, bounded or otherwise.

3. Let D be a line of Π, and let $a, b \in \Pi$.

For every $x \in D$, let $f(x) = d(a, x) + d(b, x)$.

Show that f is convex. For which points x of D does the function f take on a minimum?

Treat similarly the maximum values of $|d(a, x) - d(b, x)|$.

4. Let A, B be two distinct parallel lines. Let $a, b \in \Pi$.

Find $x \in A$, $y \in B$ such that $d(x, a) + d(x, y) + d(y, b)$ is a minimum.

Consider the same problem with the additional condition that the line $\Delta(x, y)$ has a given direction δ.

5. Let $(a_i, b_i)(i = 1, 2, 3)$ be three isometric pairs of points in Π. Can you find three lines D_i and a pair of points (a, b) such that, for every i, (a_i, b_i) is the image of (a, b) in the symmetry with respect to D_i?

6. Let f (resp. g) be the rotation through an angle θ about x (resp. $-\theta$ about y). What is $g \circ f$?

7. Let (a_1, a_2, a_3) be a triplet of distinct points of Π. Let $\widehat{a_i}$ denote its angles (see following chapter). What is the product $f_3 \circ f_2 \circ f_1$, when f_i denotes the rotation of angle $\widehat{a_i}$ about a_i?

8. Let $a, b \in \Pi$, with $a \neq b$, and let f be a rotation with centre a.

(a) Determine the set $\mathscr{B}$ of rotations g with centre b such that $g \circ f$ is a rotation.

(b) What is the set of centres for the rotations $g \circ f$ (where $g \in \mathscr{B}$)?

9. Let $\mathscr{G}$ be a subgroup of $\mathscr{I}_0$. Show that if $\mathscr{G}$ contains at least one axial symmetry, then $\mathscr{G}$ is generated by its axial symmetries.

10. Find the orders of the groups of isometries of the following sets: vertices of an equilateral triangle; square; rectangle; rhombus.

11. Let A, B be two lines of Π, and let $a \in A$, $b \in B$.

Find the even isometries f such that $f(a) \in A$ and $f(b) \in B$.

12. Let Z be the metric subspace of R consisting of the set of integers.

Determine all possible partitions of Z into two isometric subsets.

13. Find all possible partitions of Π into pairs of isometric subsets.

14. Let A, B be two subsets of Π such that $A \cap B$ contains at least two points x_1 and x_2. Show that if there is an isometry f from A onto B whose restriction to $A \cap B$ is the identity, then either f is the identity map or $A \cap B = (A \cup B) \cap \Delta(x_1, x_2)$.

What is the connection between this property and the fact that the edge of a folded piece of paper is always a line segment?

15. Let f be an even similitude of Π, and λ an arbitrary number. For $x \in \Pi$, let $f_\lambda(x)$ be the point dividing $(x, f(x))$ in the ratio λ. What can you say about the map $x \to f_\lambda(x)$?

16. Let A_i $(i = 1, 2, 3)$ be three lines in Π, let $a_i \in A_i$ $(i = 1, 2, 3)$.

(a) Let $\mathscr{F}$ be the set of even similitudes such that $f(a_i) \in A_i$ $(i = 1, 2, 3)$.

Show that, either all the elements of $\mathscr{F}$ have the same centre a, or they are all translations.

If x is any point of Π with $x \neq a$, what can be said about the set of all points $f(x)$, where f ranges over $\mathscr{F}$?

(b) Let $\mathscr{G}$ be the set of even similitudes g such that $a_i \in g(A_i)$ $(i = 1, 2, 3)$.

What is the relationship between $\mathscr{F}$ and $\mathscr{G}$?

17. Let $(0, a, b)$ be a triplet of Π with $a, b \neq 0$. Characterize the mappings f from Π into itself which have the property that, for any x, the triplet $(0, x, f(x))$ is either the triplet $(0, 0, 0)$ or the image of $(0, a, b)$ under an even similitude.

18. Let E be an arbitrary subset and $\mathscr{G}$ an abelian transformation group which is simply transitive on E.

Let a, b be two points of E, and let f be a mapping of E into itself with the property that for every $x \in$ E, there exists some $g \in \mathscr{G}$ such that $g(a) = x$ and $g(b) = f(x)$.

What can you say about f?

19. By means of Exercise 9 in Chapter II, obtain the classification of closed groups of dilations of Π (and R^n) given in §53.

Exercises on conjugates. Recall that if f and g are two transformations of a set E, then the *conjugate* of f by g is the transformation $g \circ f \circ g^{-1}$. It maps $g(x)$ to $g(f(x))$.

20. Let f be the homothetic transformation with centre a and ratio k. Show that the conjugate of f by any similitude g (and more generally by any affine transformation) is a homothetic transformation with centre $g(0)$ and ratio k. (First treat the case where $g(0) = 0$, and the case where g is a translation.)

21. Show that the conjugate of the translation $x \to x + b$ by a linear transformation g is the translation $x \to x + g(b)$.

22. Let f be the symmetry whose axis is D and g any similitude. Show that the conjugate of f by g is the symmetry whose axis is $g(D)$.

23. Let f_i be symmetries with axes D_i ($i = 1, 2, \ldots, n$) and g be an arbitrary similitude. Show that the conjugate of $f_1 \circ f_2 \circ \cdots \circ f_n$ by g is $f_1' \circ f_2' \circ \cdots \circ f_n'$, where f_i' is the symmetry whose axis is $g(D_i)$.

24. Let f be a rotation about a through an angle θ. Show that its conjugate under a similitude g is the rotation about $g(a)$ through $\pm \theta$ (depending on whether g is even or odd).

Chapter V

Angles

1. The group of angles

57. DIFFICULTIES IN DEFINING AN ANGLE

When teaching geometry, the concept of angle probably causes more problems and provokes more discussion than anything else.

Difficulties are partly due to imprecise terminology, partly to muddled thinking, and the position is hardly improved by the use of the word "angle" for various related but distinct concepts such as plane sector, pair of half-lines, angular measure. Even so, we must not detract from the fact that there are very real mathematical difficulties inherent in the question.

Perhaps the most simple definition would run as follows:

An angle with vertex 0 (or a plane sector) is the intersection of two closed half-planes whose frontiers pass through 0 and are distinct.

Although admirably suited to design work, drawing, measuring with a protractor (in short, the "intuitive" geometry taught up to the age of 12 or 13), trouble occurs with this definition when several rather large angles have to be added. At this point, alas, all too often, the explanations degenerate into waffle about angles (greater than 360°) spiralling upon themselves. This only obscures the issue and frightens people off.

Some of the difficulties can be avoided by refining our idea of angle. Instead of being part of the plane, it will be an ordered pair of half-lines with a common origin. Difficulties still remain over addition, and it is by attempting to overcome these that we are first led to introducing an equivalence relation on the set of ordered pairs of half-lines, defining the addition on the associated quotient set. Although perfectly correct, this method makes heavy going.

To ease matters, some authors postulate the existence of a "measure" on the set of ordered pairs of half-lines (unopposed), and the additivity of this measure on "small" angles. Apparently rigorous, such an axiomatization must nevertheless fail because it does not take into account the essential difference between the group of angles and the additive group R. For example, in the former, $\theta + \theta = 0$ does not imply $\theta = 0$. What is worse, even at the very beginning of elementary geometry, it is so inflexible that it does not allow the elementary operation of doubling: $\theta \rightarrow 2\theta$.

In any proper definition, angles are fairly abstract things. The problem we have to face in teaching, is making the abstraction accessible and adopting a definition in which all terms are intuitive.

For example, to an algebraist, the following definition would be perfect:

First notice that the set $\mathscr{T}$ of translations is a normal subgroup of the group $\mathscr{I}^+$ of even isometries (conjugate of a translation by an isometry is a translation); define the group of angles as $\mathscr{I}^+/\mathscr{T}$ and take the angle of an even isometry f as the canonical image of f in the factor group. For a pair of half-lines (A, B) in Π, define angle (A, B) (written $\widehat{AB}$) to be the angle of f, where f is the even isometry transforming A to B.

The disadvantage of a definition of this kind is that it requires a fair degree of mathematical sophistication and a good knowledge of group theory. We shall opt for a less abstract definition, identifying angles with rotations about a point 0; eventually, of course, we shall need to show that this definition is independent of the choice of 0.

Before completing this discussion, it is, perhaps, timely to point out that we have built up a considerable part of our geometry without any recourse to angles: affine structure; Pythagorean theorem; theory of similitudes—all have been established without angle or congruence. In teaching, there has been a tendency to abuse angles, probably for historical reasons. It was a primitive term in Euclid's axiomatization, and for a long time, the "parallel postulate" was expressed in terms of angles. Almost inevitably, his successors carried on in the same vein and, once they had a fair grasp of the notion of an orientated angle and the angle of a line pair, proceeded to make an entirely unwarranted universal use of them.

There are strong reasons for doing away with this and developing almost the whole of our geometry without measuring a single angle. Although it is an essential tool of analysis and applied mathematics, angle is often merely baggage, as far as geometry is concerned, and sometimes even a source of error.

58. DEFINITION AND NOTATION

Definition 58.1. For every $0 \in \Pi$, *a rotation about* 0 *is called* an angle with vertex at 0. *If* (A_1, A_2) *is a pair of half-lines whose origin is* 0, *the rotation about* 0 *taking* A_1 *to* A_2 *is called the angle formed by the pair; it is written* $\widehat{A_1A_2}$.

The set of angles with vertex at 0 is, then, the set of rotations about 0 and is therefore a commutative group. As regards angles, it is convenient to write this group operation additively. Besides being in accordance with historical notation, this fits in well with the close relationship between the addition of real numbers and the addition of angles that we shall develop later.

Comparison of angles which have different vertices. Our concept of angle would be rather useless if it did not lend itself to comparison of angles with different vertices. The translation allows us to do this.

For $a, b \in \Pi$, the translation $I_{b, a}$ taking a to b is an isomorphism from the pointed plane (Π, a) onto (Π, b) preserving both vector and metric structure. This isomorphism is transitive in the sense that for $a, b, c \in \Pi$,

$$I_{c\,a,} = I_{c, b} \circ I_{b, a}$$

As rotations are defined in terms of lines and distances, the isomorphism $I_{b,a}$ induces an isomorphism of the additive group of angles at a onto the corresponding group at b. (For convenience, this isomorphism will also be denoted by $I_{b,a}$.) At this point, we make use of a device that is used for instance to define the set N of natural numbers.

We choose an arbitrary origin a in Π and identify every angle with vertex b with the corresponding angle with vertex a obtained by the isomorphism $I_{b,a}$; the transitivity of the isomorphisms I guarantees the consistency of this identification. Now, if A_1, A_2 are two arbitrary half-lines with origin a, we see[6] that as the isomorphism $I_{b,a}$ of (Π, a) onto (Π, b) transforms each A_i onto the parallel half-line B_i with origin b,

$$\widehat{A_1 A_2} = \widehat{B_1 B_2}$$

(bearing in mind the identification that we have adopted).

These considerations justify the following definition, which only apparently depends on the origin 0 chosen.

Definition 58.2. In the pointed plane $(\Pi, 0)$, *the angle of a pair* (D_1, D_2) *of half-lines of arbitrary origin is defined to be the angle with vertex 0 of the half-lines* D_1', D_2' *with origin 0 which are parallel to* D_1, D_2 *respectively.*

It is written $\widehat{D_1 D_2}$, and the additive group of angles is denoted by $\mathscr{A}$.

Consequent notation. Other notation is usefully employed in connection with the notation $\widehat{D_1 D_2}$. In general, let E be a set of mathematical entities and suppose that with each element of E we associate a half-line of Π or a set of parallel half-lines. We can extend our notation and write $\widehat{xy}$ for the angle formed by one of the half-lines associated with x with one of the half-lines associated with y, this being valid for every $x, y \in$ E.

For example, with every vector $x \neq 0$ in $(\Pi, 0)$, we can associate the half-line $D(0, x)$; with an orientated line D, the positive half-lines in D. Thus, we can speak of the angle $\widehat{xD}$. By the same token, the simplified notation $\widehat{abc}$ denotes the angle formed by $D(b, a)$, $D(b, c)$, where a, b, c is a triplet of points with $a \neq b$, $c \neq b$.

Zero angle and straight angle. In the additive group of angles $\mathscr{A}$, the neutral element will be denoted by 0, and the straight angle associated with the symmetry centre 0 by $\bar{\omega}$.

If (D_1, D_2) is a pair of half-lines with the same origin, the following equivalences hold:

$$(\widehat{D_1 D_2} = 0) \Leftrightarrow (D_1 = D_2)$$

$$(\widehat{D_1 D_2} = \bar{\omega}) \Leftrightarrow (D_1 \text{ and } D_2 \text{ are opposite})$$

Furthermore

$$\bar{\omega} + \bar{\omega} = 0 \quad \text{or} \quad -\bar{\omega} = \bar{\omega}$$

Chasles' Formula. Let A, B, C be three arbitrary half-lines whose origin is at 0. Then the

---

6 Families $(I_{b,a}')$ of isomorphisms transitive on the set of pointed planes (Π, x) for which this equality need not hold can be easily constructed. The family that we have chosen is the only "natural" one.

rotation taking A to C is the product of that taking A to B with that taking B to C. In other words:

$$\widehat{AC} = \widehat{AB} + \widehat{BC}$$

In particular, $\widehat{AB} + \widehat{BA} = \widehat{AA} = 0$, and so $\widehat{AB} = -\widehat{BA}$.

More generally, we have

$$\widehat{D_1 D_n} = \widehat{D_1 D_2} + \widehat{D_2 D_3} + \cdots + \widehat{D_{n-1} D_n}$$

whenever $(D_1, D_2, \ldots, D_n)$ is a finite sequence of half-lines with the same origin 0.

This relation is called Chasles' formula. It clearly extends to the case of half-lines with arbitrary origins (by parallelism).

59. THE SUM OF THE ANGLES OF A CLOSED PLANE POLYGON

Let P be a closed plane polygon with n vertices, i.e. a sequence $(a_1, a_2, \ldots, a_n)$ of points of Π, defined up to a circular permutation. Here we suppose that, for every i, $a_i \neq a_{i+1}$ (and also $a_n \neq a_1$). Thus we can write $\delta_i = $ the half-line $D(a_i, a_{i+1})$.

The angle $\widehat{\delta_{i-1} \delta_i}$ is called the *exterior angle* of P at the vertex a_i and the angle $\widehat{a_{i-1} a_i a_{i+1}}$ is called the *angle* of P at a_i.

Proposition 59.1. The sum of the exterior angles of a closed plane polygon is 0.
Proof. For by Chasles' relation,

$$\widehat{\delta_1 \delta_2} + \widehat{\delta_2 \delta_3} + \cdots + \widehat{\delta_n \delta_1} = \widehat{\delta_1 \delta_1} = 0$$

Corollary 59.2. The sum of the angles of every closed plane polygon is either 0 or $\bar{\omega}$ depending on whether the number n of vertices is even or odd.

For letting δ'_{i-1} be the half-line $D(a_i, a_{i-1})$, we have $\widehat{\delta_{i-1} \delta'_{i-1}} = \bar{\omega}$.
Thus,

$$\widehat{a_{i-1} a_i a_{i+1}} = \widehat{\delta'_{i-1} \delta_{i-1}} + \widehat{\delta_{i-1} \delta_i} = \bar{\omega} + \widehat{\delta_{i-1} \delta_i}$$

Hence the sum of these angles is $n\bar{\omega} + 0 = 0$ or $\bar{\omega}$ depending on whether n is even or odd (because $\bar{\omega} + \bar{\omega} = 0$).

In particular the sum of the angles of a triplet (a_1, a_2, a_3) is $\bar{\omega}$. When we have defined the notion of orientation, we shall give a precise version of this result and show that the three angles determined by such a triplet always have the same orientation.

Angles and similitudes

60. ANGLES UNDER SYMMETRIES

Lemma 60.1. Let σ be a symmetry whose axis passes through 0. If (A, B) is a pair of half-lines whose origin is at 0, then

$$\widehat{A'B'} = -\widehat{AB} \qquad where \quad A' = \sigma(A) \quad and \quad B' = \sigma(B)$$

Proof. Let D be one of the two half-lines with origin 0 lying in the axis of σ, and let τ be the symmetry which interchanges D and A'. The rotation $\tau.\sigma$ transforms D to A' and A to D, and so

$$\widehat{DA'} = \widehat{AD}$$

Similarly,
$$\widehat{DB'} = \widehat{BD}$$

Hence

$$\widehat{A'B'} = \widehat{A'D} + \widehat{DB'} = \widehat{DA} + \widehat{BD} = \widehat{BA} = -\widehat{AB}$$

61. ANGLES UNDER SIMILITUDES

Proposition 61.1. If (A, B) *is a pair of half-lines of* Π, *and if f is a similitude of* Π, *then*

$$\widehat{f(A)f(B)} = \widehat{AB} \qquad \textit{if f is even}$$

$$\widehat{f(A)f(B)} = -\widehat{AB} \qquad \textit{if f is odd}$$

Proof. We know that every similitude f is the product of a dilation of positive ratio with an isometry fixing 0 of the same parity as f. As such dilations preserve the direction of half-lines, angles are preserved and we need only consider the case where f is an isometry fixing 0.

Furthermore, as the images of parallel half-lines under f are again parallel half-lines, there is no loss of generality in assuming that A, B have the same origin 0.

When f is odd, it is an axial symmetry, and Lemma 60.1 shows that

$$\widehat{f(A)f(B)} = -\widehat{AB}$$

When f is even, it is the product of two axial symmetries and the required result comes from the equality $-(-\widehat{AB}) = \widehat{AB}$.

62. CHARACTERIZATION OF ROTATIONS

Proposition 62.1. Let θ *be an angle,* $a \in \Pi$, *and let f be a mapping from* Π *into itself. The mapping f is the rotation about a through the angle* θ *if and only if* $f(a) = a$, *and*

$$d(a, x) = d(a, f(x)), \quad \widehat{xaf(x)} = \theta, \quad \textit{for all } x \neq a$$

Proof. Clearly the rotation about a of angle θ has these properties. On the other hand, for every $x \neq a$, the relations

$$d(a, x) = d(a, y) \quad \text{and} \quad \widehat{xay} = \theta$$

define a unique y. Hence any mapping f possessing the given properties is the rotation about a through the angle θ.

Proposition 62.2. Let $a \in \Pi$, *and let f be a mapping of* Π *into itself.*
The mapping f is a rotation about a if and only if

1. $f(a) = a$.

2. For every $x \neq a$, $d(a, x) = d(a, f(x))$.

3. For every $x, y \neq a$, $\widehat{xay} = \widehat{f(x)af(y)}$.

Proof. By Prop. 61.1, every rotation about a satisfies property 3. Properties 1 and 2 are obvious.

Conversely, if f satisfies property 3, Chasles' relation gives

$$\widehat{xaf(x)} = \widehat{xay} + \widehat{yaf(y)} + \widehat{f(y)af(x)} = \widehat{yaf(y)} \text{ for all } x, y \neq a$$

Thus, $\widehat{xaf(x)} = $ constant θ, and Prop. 62.1 applies.

63. CHARACTERIZATION OF SIMILITUDES

Proposition 63.1. Let X be a non-collinear subset of Π, and let f be an injection of X into Π. Then if

$$\widehat{f(x)f(y)f(z)} = \widehat{xyz} \quad (resp. - \widehat{xyz})$$

for all distinct x, y, $z \in \Pi$, f is the restriction to X of an unique similitude of Π. This similitude is even (resp. odd).

Proof. By taking, if necessary, the composition of f with an axial symmetry, we see that we can assume that f preserves angles.

Now choose two distinct points $a, b \in X$ and let g be the even similitude which transforms (a, b) to $(f(a), f(b))$.

The mapping $h = g^{-1} \circ f$ of X into Π fixes a and b, and preserves angles. It follows that for every $x \in X$ such that $x \notin \Delta(a, b)$, the lines $\Delta(a, x), \Delta(b, x)$ intersect and are parallel to $\Delta(a, h(x)), \Delta(b, h(x))$, respectively. Thus, $h(x) = x$.

This means that h is the identity outside $\Delta(a, b)$ and, as by hypothesis there is at least one point $c \notin \Delta(a, b)$, the same reasoning shows that h is the identity outside $\Delta(a, c)$. Hence, h is the identity on X and, as X contains three non-collinear points, the only similitude of Π which extends h is the identity of Π. In other words, f is the restriction of g to X, and this similitude g is unique.

It may be noticed that this proof is based on that of Prop. 27.2. Examination of that proof shows that the requirement that f is one-one is not really necessary for the truth of our proposition, but the statement becomes somewhat complicated if we leave it out. However, the condition that X is not collinear is essential.

Remark 63.2. In particular, Prop. 63.1 applies to the case where X is a set of three non-collinear points a, b, c. This provides in rigorous form one of the four cases for "similarity of triangles". Prop. 61.1 gives a second case and from these, we can rigorously derive two cases of congruence of triangles.

Again, we point out that we have not really needed these cases of congruence and similarity at any stage of our development. We would even claim that a case has been made that they should not be used other than for those specially constructed problems designed for them. A few techniques from analysis or vector spaces replaces them with advantages all round.

64. Dividing an Angle by 2

Proposition 64.1. *If α is an angle, the equation $2x = \alpha$ has exactly two solutions and these solutions differ by $\bar{\omega}$.*

In fact, if A, B are two half-lines whose origin is at 0, the half-lines D originating at 0 which satisfy

$$2\widehat{AD} = \widehat{AB} \quad (i.e.\ \widehat{AD} = \widehat{DB})$$

are the half-lines in the axis of the symmetry σ interchanging A and B.

Proof. Let A, B be two half-lines originating at 0 such that $\widehat{AB} = \alpha$.

The relation $2\widehat{AD} = \widehat{AB}$ can be written as

$$2\widehat{AD} = \widehat{AD} + \widehat{DB} \quad \text{or} \quad \widehat{AD} = \widehat{DB}$$

This is satisfied if D is either of the half-lines D_1, D_2 lying on the axis of σ (Lemma 60.1).

Conversely, suppose that $\widehat{AD} = \widehat{DB}$. Let B′ be the line symmetric to A with respect to the line in which D lies. Lemma 60.1 shows that $\widehat{AD} = \widehat{DB'}$, which yields $\widehat{DB'} = \widehat{DB}$, i.e. B = B′.

This shows that the line carrying D is indeed the axis of σ and so either $D = D_1$ or $D = D_2$.

Corollary. 1. *The equation $2x = 0$ has only solutions 0 and $\bar{\omega}$.*

2. *The equation $2x = \bar{\omega}$ has two solutions (called right angles). Moreover, $(A \perp B) \Leftrightarrow (\widehat{AB}$ is a right angle).*

Remark. At present, we do not know how to solve equations in $\mathscr{A}$ of the form $nx = 0$ or $nx = \alpha$ ($n \in \mathbf{Z}$). Once we have dealt with the measurement of angles, this will become abundantly clear. However, it is by no means necessary for elementary geometry.

65. Angles Formed by a Pair of Lines

Definition 65.1. *Let (A, B) be a pair of lines passing through 0. The angles formed by the pair are defined to be the rotations about 0 taking A to B.*

It follows immediately that there are exactly two such angles and they are obtained by taking a half-line in A with each of the two half-lines in B. Their difference is $\bar{\omega}$.

This definition can be extended to an arbitrary pair of lines or directions by parallelism, and the following example, which is also helpful for grasping the underlying ideas, shows that it can be generalized in other directions as well.

Let A be a family of half-lines with a common origin at 0 which is globally invariant under a subgroup $\mathscr{G}$ of $\mathscr{R}_0$. Let $\rho \in \mathscr{R}_0$, $B = \rho(A)$. The rotations ρ' such that $B = \rho'(A)$ form the coset $\rho \circ \mathscr{G}$, thereby giving a multiplicity of angles for the pair (A, B). To attach a unique pseudo-angle to (A, B), we would have to take an element of the quotient $\mathscr{R}_0/\mathscr{G}$. In the case where A is the pair of half-lines on a given line, for example, $\mathscr{G}$ is the subgroup $\{0, \bar{\omega}\}$ of $\mathscr{R}_0$ ($\mathscr{R}_0$ being identifiable with $\mathscr{A}$ of Definition 58.2).

Notice that if α_1 and α_2 are the angles formed by the pair (A, B), the relation $\alpha_2 = \alpha_1 + \bar{\omega}$ yields $2\alpha_2 = 2\alpha_1$. Since, conversely, $2x = 2\alpha$, implies $x = \alpha_1$ or $x = \alpha_1 + \bar{\omega}$, it is preferable to associate with (A, B) the double angle $2\alpha_1 \, (= 2\alpha_2)$ rather than the angles α_1, α_2. This spares a lot of fiddling difficulties when it comes to dealing with angles between lines.

To take one illustration, let A, B be two lines passing through 0 and let α be one of the angles formed by (A, B). The product of the symmetries with respect to A and B is a rotation f, say, about 0 and we proceed to determine its angle.

If A_1 is one of the half-lines in A with origin 0, and B_1 is the half-line of B at the same origin such that $\widehat{A_1 B_1} = \alpha$, we have $f(A_1) = $ image of A_1 under symmetry with respect to B.

By Lemma 60.1,

$$\widehat{A_1 f(A_1)} = \widehat{A_1 B_1} + \widehat{B_1 f(A_1)} = \widehat{A_1 B_1} - \widehat{B_1 A_1} = 2\alpha$$

i.e. the angle of f is 2α.

Orientation

66. Difficulties about orientation

With that of angle, orientation is considered to be one of the hardest concepts to teach. In default of a true mathematical definition, it is usually explained by recourse to a little man with an infallible memory who is impaled on the plane. Alternatively, the question is referred to three mutually perpendicular fingers on the right or left hand, depending on the country of origin.

Now while the theory of angles presents very real difficulty, as far as geometry is concerned, orientation is easily developed by reference to the isometry group.

One of the basic obstacles to a proper appreciation of orientation lies in the type of configuration involved. This generally consists of a set of pairs (A, B) of half-lines, not collinear, but with the same origin. With each such pair (A, B) we naturally associate the opposite pair (B, A), and these two pairs have opposite orientation. Because of this, there is a tendency to blur the distinction between the concept of an ordered pair (or more generally an ordered set) and the concept of orientation. Certainly, the two are related, and related in a very precise way. However, this is only really appreciated through a clear understanding of orientation based on definitions totally independent of order relations.

67. Orientation of subsets of Π

To begin, we take some examples.
1. In Π, there are sets of three points where the mutual distances between the points are 2, 3, 4. Such a set cannot be collinear because $4 < 2 + 3$ (Corollary 39.4 and Prop. 39.5).

Let E be the set of such subsets of Π.

This set is stable under the isometry group $\mathscr{I}$ of Π. Furthermore $\mathscr{I}$ is simply transitive in its operation on E because, for every $X_1, X_2 \in E$, there is obviously a unique mapping f from X_1 onto X_2 which is an isometry, and, as X is not collinear, f extends to a unique isometry of Π into itself (Theorem 45.6).

We shall say that X_1 and X_2 have the *same orientation* if the isometry f of Π such that

$X_2 = f(X_1)$ is even (otherwise we say that X_1 and X_2 have *opposite orientation*). The fact that $\mathscr{I}^+$ is a group immediately implies that this is an equivalence relation on E.

If X_1, X_2 have opposite orientations, and so do X_2, X_3, then X_1, X_3 have the same orientation, because the product of two odd isometries is an even isometry.

Thus, the equivalence relation on E has two classes: the images under $\mathscr{I}^+$ and $\mathscr{I}^-$ of an arbitrary element X_0 of E.

Next, let us see what we mean by calling an orientation positive or negative. Take an arbitrary element X_0 of E and call it the basis of reference; an element X of E is said to have *positive orientation* (resp. *negative* orientation) if X_0 and X have the same (resp. opposite) orientation. Strictly speaking, we should say that X has a positive orientation with respect to the reference base. However, when there can be no possible confusion over the basis in question, this omission is justified.

Quite clearly, the sign of the orientation is unchanged if we replace the reference base X_0 by any other of the same orientation.

Other analogous examples

2. More generally, let A be a non-collinear subset of Π with the property that the identity is the only isometry of A onto itself. Let E be the set of subsets of Π of the form $f(A)$ (where $f \in \mathscr{I}$).

Evidently, E is stable under $\mathscr{I}$ and $\mathscr{I}$ acts transitively on E.

We can, then, repeat for E everything that was done in the previous example. In particular, we can take A to be a *polarized half-plane*, i.e. the union of an open half-line D and one of the open half-planes associated with the line on D.

3. (A further extension of this process.) Let A be a non-collinear subset of Π such that every isometry from A onto itself is even (in the sense that the extension to Π is an even isometry). If E is defined as above, E is stable under $\mathscr{I}$ and, for all X_1, X_2 of E, there exists at least one isometry $f \in \mathscr{I}$ transforming X_1 to X_2. By hypothesis, all such isometries have the same parity.

Defining orientation for the elements of E is now an easy matter and so is the comparison of orientations. The whole of the above theory applies.

As an example, we could take A to be the union of two opposite sides of a square and one of its diagonals (letter Z). Alternatively, we could take the set of translates of an interval $[a, b]$ under translations t^n $(n \in Z)$, where t is a translation which is neither parallel nor perpendicular to $[a, b]$.

68. ORIENTATION OF OTHER GEOMETRICAL ENTITIES ASSOCIATED WITH Π

We have already encountered geometrical entities which are associated with Π but are not subsets of Π: pair of points; triplet of points; pair of half-lines; orientated line; transformation; angle; etc. We now show how to define an orientation for some of these.

1. (a) Let E be the set of pairs (A, B) in Π in which A, B are perpendicular half-lines having the same origin. This set is stable under $\mathscr{I}$, and the action of $\mathscr{I}$ is transitive. We can repeat for E everything that we did in the previous examples, and the condition that (A, B) and (A', B') have the same orientation becomes the condition $\widehat{AB} = \widehat{A'B'}$.

However, this time we have something new. This is the existence of an involutory transformation (A, B) → (B, A) of E, which associates with each element (A, B) of E its *opposite* element (B, A). But the isometry taking (A, B) to (B, A) is an axial symmetry. Hence opposing pairs (A, B), (B, A) have opposite orientations.

(b) More generally, take E as the set of pairs (A, B) of half-lines such that A, B have the same origin and $\widehat{AB} = \pm\,\theta$ (where θ is some given angle other than 0 and $\bar{\omega}$).

(c) (A less familiar example.) Take E as the set of pairs (D, x), where D is an orientated line in Π and x is a point distance 1 from D.

(d) Here E is the set of triplets (x, y, z) isometric to a given non-collinear triplet (a, b, c). A case of particular interest arises when $\| b - a \| = \| c - a \| = 1$ and $\Delta(a, b) \perp \Delta(a, c)$. In this case the vectors b, c of (Π, a) are an orthonormal basis of (Π, a), and E is the set of orthonormal reference bases of Π. The definition of a positive frame of reference obtained in this way coincides with the classical definition.

2. Next we have two examples which show that orientation is quite a separate notion from that of isometry. They will also show us how to compare the orientations of any pair of non-collinear triplets or any pair of non-collinear half-lines.

Let a denote the group of affine transformations of Π and a_+ denote the subgroup of affine transformations with positive determinant (we assume that the reader knows what is meant by this).

(a) Let E be the set of *non-collinear triplets* (x, y, z) of points of Π. The set E is stable under the action of a and the action is simply transitive.

We say that (x, y, z), (x', y', z') have the same orientation if the element f of a taking (x, y, z) to (x', y', z') is in a_+.

Now because the determinant of $f \circ g$, where $f, g \in a$, is the product of the determinant of f with the determinant of g, the affine groups a can be studied in the same way as the group of isometries. The results are virtually parallel.

Notice that in the particular case where the affine transformation f is an isometry, its determinant is positive or negative depending on whether it is even or odd. The orientation that we have just defined is therefore compatible with the one defined in example 1d above.

As in example 1(a), something new emerges; namely, that with every triple (x, y, z) of E we can associate six triples obtained from it by permutation, and the orientations of these various triplets are related as follows.

Lemma 11. If a triplet is obtained from the triplet (x, y, z) by a transposition, then the two triplets have opposite orientation.

Proof. We remind the reader that a transposition is a permutation in which two symbols are interchanged and all other symbols are fixed. To demonstrate the proof, let us take, as an example, the element $f \in a$ taking x, y, z to x, z, y. This is simply the oblique symmetry with direction parallel to $\Delta(y, z)$ whose axis passes through x and the midpoint of (y, z), and its determinant is -1.

(b) Let E be the set of those pairs (A, B) of half-lines which are not collinear but have the same origin. Again E is stable under a and the action of a is transitive (without being simply transitive). Furthermore, if $f \in a$ transforms (A, B) into (A, B), then

relative to the system of axes (A, B), f has the form

$$(\xi, \eta) \to (u\xi, v\eta) \quad \text{where } u, v > 0$$

In other words, the determinant of f is positive.

Thus, we see that if (A, B), $(A', B') \in E$, all maps transforming (A, B) to (A', B') have determinants with the same sign, and this enables us to apply the methods used in the previous examples. One of the facts that immediately emerges is that opposite pairs (A, B), (B, A) have opposite orientations.

Conclusion. From all those preceding examples, it becomes apparent that the basic requirement for an orientation is a triple $(E, \mathscr{G}, \mathscr{G}^+)$ where E is some set, $\mathscr{G}$ is a transitive group of transformations of E and $\mathscr{G}^+$ is a normal subgroup of $\mathscr{G}$ of index 2 having the property that it contains every transformation fixing some point of E. (This last property is automatically satisfied if $\mathscr{G}^+$ contains the subgroup fixing any given point x.)

69. ELEMENTARY APPROACH TO THE ORIENTATION OF PAIRS OF NON-COLLINEAR HALF-LINES

From the point of view of teaching, we ought to avoid using the affine group when it comes to orientating a pair of non-collinear half-lines. The following method involves a simpler approach.

Let E be the set of pairs (A, B) of half-lines of Π which are not collinear but have the same origin. If (A, B), $(A', B') \in E$, we say that (A, B) and (A', B') have the same orientation when the *even* isometry f taking A to A' maps B onto a half-line $f(B)$ which is on the same side of the line as A' as the half-line B' (i.e. in the same half-plane defined by this line).

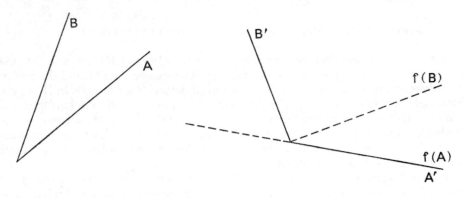

As every isometry transforms half-planes into half-planes, and the isometries are a group, this defines an equivalence relation on E. Clearly, there are exactly two equivalence classes (consider the pairs (A, X) for some fixed A) and we are therefore in a position to talk of bases of reference, positive or negative orientation, as before.

Notice that orientation is preserved by dilations of positive ratio, even isometries and, consequently, even similitudes. On the contrary, the symmetry σ about the line containing A transforms (A, B) into a pair with opposite orientation. Since all odd similitudes

f compose with σ to give an even similitude, it follows that whenever f is odd, $(f(\mathrm{A}), f(\mathrm{B}))$ and (A, B) have opposite orientations.

Orientation of angles

Let θ, θ' be any two angles other than 0 or $\bar{\omega}$. We say that θ and θ' have the same orientation if there exist pairs (A, B), $(\mathrm{A}', \mathrm{B}')$ in the above set E such that $\widehat{\mathrm{AB}} = \theta$, $\widehat{\mathrm{A}'\mathrm{B}'} = \theta'$, and (A, B), $(\mathrm{A}'\,\mathrm{B}')$ have the same orientation.

This defines an equivalence relation on the set of angles different from 0 or $\bar{\omega}$, and there are exactly two classes.

Proposition 69.1. If (x, y, z) is a non-collinear triplet, then the three angles $\widehat{xyz}, \widehat{yzx}, \widehat{zxy}$ all have the same orientation.

Proof. It is sufficient to prove the proposition for the angles $\widehat{xyz}, \widehat{yzx}$.

Let x' be a point on the perpendicular bisector of (y, z) which is on the same side of $\Delta(y, z)$ as x. Clearly $\widehat{xyz}$ and $\widehat{x'yz}$ have the same orientation, as do $\widehat{yzx}$ and $\widehat{yzx'}$.

But $\widehat{x'yz} = -\widehat{x'zy}$ (by symmetry), and so $\widehat{x'yz} = \widehat{yzx'}$.

The result now follows.

Remark. We used the metric structure of Π for this elementary approach to orientation. This is somewhat unsatisfactory because the affine structure would have sufficed. However, it turns out that even the affine structure is more than we need because it is quite possible to provide a coherent development of orientation using just Axioms I and II. We suggest that this should be done as an exercise.

70. Relation between orientation and continuous deformations

We treated orientation from an algebraic point of view because it is impossible to make proper use of continuity at an elementary level. The true reasons behind the choice of definitions and why they work are of a topological nature. For example, in Π, we could show that the triplets (x, y, z), (x', y', z') have the same orientation only if there exists a continuous family of triplets (non-collinear) linking the first to the second, or, more precisely, if under the natural topology, there exists an arc in the set of such triplets having the two given triplets as end points. An analogous result holds for the orientation of pairs on non-collinear half-lines.

In fact, because orientation is defined by specifying the appropriate subgroup of the group of transformations, all we really have to do is investigate how this subgroup can arise.

The transformation groups $\mathscr{G}$ which are studied in geometry invariably act on topological spaces—generally finite dimensional varieties. More to the point, they themselves have a topology compatible with the group structure (group multiplication and taking inverses are continuous operations).

For example, in the case of the group of linear transformations of an n-dimensional Euclidean space, this topology is conveniently obtained by identifying the matrix

coefficients (a_{ij}) of the transformations (relative to some basis) with points of R^N, where $N = n^2$, and taking that topology induced by R^N.

In such a topological group $\mathscr{G}$, we can speak of arcs and connected components. The group $\mathscr{G}^+$ is then the connected component of the identity element e and, in the usual cases, this is simply the set of elements x of $\mathscr{G}$ which can be the extremities of arcs originating at e. We then prove that $\mathscr{G}^+$ is a normal subgroup of $\mathscr{G}$ and define the quotient group $\mathscr{G}/\mathscr{G}^+$ to be the group of orientations of $\mathscr{G}$.

In the most common cases—and for all the cases that we had in mind— this quotient group has order 2. It can happen, however, that this is not so. For example, if $\mathscr{G}$ is the group of differentiable transformations of the set consisting of the union of two disjoint circles, $\mathscr{G}/\mathscr{G}^+$ is of order 8. If it so happens that $\mathscr{G}$ is connected, $\mathscr{G}^+ = \mathscr{G}$ and $\mathscr{G}/\mathscr{G}^+$ is trivial; the group of projectivities of the projective plane is an example of this.

At this point, we shall examine the particular case of the isometry group. In so doing, we may hope to remove some of the confusion existing between the notions of transformation and continuous deformation.

71. CONTINUOUS DEFORMATIONS

A child experiences very real difficulties in understanding the notion of isometry because so few[7] pure examples are found in the physical world. Generally, his everyday experience furnishes him more with examples of continuous families of isometries, which we shall call continuous deformations. His difficulties are increased by the fact that neither the plane nor any portion of it has a "discrete" structure, and it is physically difficult to discern in a concrete model the image of a point under an isometry.

This second difficulty can be eased somewhat by studying first only transformations of finite subsets of the plane, and then going on to use a representation of the points of the plane—or "molecules" of the concrete example—by means of coordinates.

As far as the first difficulty is concerned, though, the only satisfactory procedure is to study the ideas of continuous deformation and isometry side by side, pinpointing the differences.

Definition 71.1. Let $\mathscr{I}$ be the set of isometries of Π.

A continuous deformation *is a map* $t \to f_t$ *of an interval* $[u, v]$ *of* R *into* $\mathscr{I}$*, continuous in the sense that, for each* $a \in \Pi$, $t \to f_t(a)$ *is a continuous map from* $[u, v]$ *into* Π.

It is easily seen that if $t \to f_t(a_i)$ is continuous for three non-collinear points a_i $(i = 1, 2, 3)$, then $t \to f_t$ is continuous. For every $a \in \Pi$ can be written uniquely as $a = \sum \alpha_i a$, (where $\sum \alpha_i = 1$) in $(\Pi, 0)$, and, as each f_t is an affine map,

$$f_t(a) = \sum \alpha_i f_t(a_i)$$

This is a continuous function, being the sum of three continuous functions.

The following proposition represents a link between orientation and continuous deformation. Incidentally, it also explains why orientations defined in terms of one plane sheet sliding on another are workable.

---

7 We might mention, however, reflection in a mirror or two copies of the same engraving.

Proposition 71.2. In any continuous deformation $t \to f_t$, the isometries f_t are either all even or all odd.

Proof. The determinant of the transformation f_t is a continuous function of t (since the coefficients of the matrix of f_t must be by hypothesis). As it is always non-zero, it must then have a constant sign, and this proves the result.

It should be mentioned that Prop. 71.2 (and proof) is still valid even if the f_t are affine transformations.

Corollary. If f_u is the identity map, each f_t is even.

Particular case. The continuous deformation of rotation.

Because we shall need to measure angles later on, we are particularly interested in continuous homomorphisms from the additive group R onto the additive group of angles. Suppose $t \to \alpha(t)$ is such a homomorphism, and let f_t be the rotation through $\alpha(t)$ about some point 0. A continuous deformation of the form $t \to f_t$ (where $t \in [0, v]$) is called a continuous rotation about 0.

The *trajectory*, or *path*, of a point under a continuous rotation is called a *circular arc*.

Notice that although we can attach a unique rotation to any continuous rotation (the rotation f_v), the converse is decidedly false.

Exercises on Chapter VI

We aim to show how some of the properties derived above from the affine structure of Π can be obtained using only Axioms I and II, provided that the cardinal α of the lines in Π satisfies $\alpha > 2$ (α is then infinite by Exercise 4, Chapter I).

Orientated direction

1. Let A, B be a pair of parallel lines. Choose, for each line, one of the two possible orientations of that line.

We say that these orientated lines have the same orientation if there exists a direction δ, not parallel to A or B, such that the projection of A onto B parallel to δ is monotonically increasing (it must be either monotonically increasing or decreasing by Corollary 6.3). Show that if this condition is satisfied for one such δ, it must be satisfied for all directions δ' not parallel to A and B. (Use Exercise 7 of Chapter I.)

2. Show that the relation described in the previous example defines an equivalence relation on the set of orientated lines which have a given direction. Show that the set breaks into two classes and the two orientated lines associated with a line lie in distinct classes.

Orientation of pairs of non-collinear half-lines with the same origin

3. Any pair (A, P), where A is an orientated line, and P one of the closed half-planes associated with A, is called an *orientated half-plane*.

Two pairs (A, P), (A', P') are said to have the same orientation if one of the following three conditions hold:

(a) A and A′ intersect and the orientations of the half-lines $(A \cap P')$, $(A' \cap P)$ inherited from those of A and A′ are opposite.

(b) A, A′ are parallel and have the same sense, and one of the half-planes P, P′ contains the other.

(c) A, A′ are parallel without having the same sense, and neither of P, P′ contains the other.

Show that this defines an equivalence relation on the set of orientated half-planes which, again, falls into two classes. Show also that the two half-planes associated with the same orientated line have opposite orientations.

[The following is perhaps a more elegant method of comparing orientations of orientated half-planes.

Take (A, P), (A′, P′) as before and define for every transversal D of A and A′ the numbers $\alpha_{A,A'}(D)$, $\beta_{P,P'}(D)$, where:

$\alpha_{A,A'}(D) = 1$ or -1, depending on whether the oblique projection of A on A′ parallel to D is monotone increasing or decreasing;

$\beta_{P,P'}(D) = 1$ or -1, depending on whether $D \cap P$ and $D \cap P'$ have the same orientation in D or not.

It can then be shown that the product of these two numbers is independent of D, and we say that (A, P), (A′, P′) have the same orientation when it takes the value 1.

The obvious relations:

$$\alpha_{A,A'} = \alpha_{A',A}, \qquad \alpha_{A,A} = 1, \qquad \alpha_{A,A''} = \alpha_{A,A'} \times \alpha_{A',A''}$$

and the analogous relations for β quickly show that this gives an equivalence relation, and that there are exactly two classes. Finally, this is the same equivalence relation as that given at the beginning of the exercise.]

4. For every pair (A, B) of non-collinear half-lines with the same origin, let $f(A, B)$ be the orientated half-plane made up by the orientated line belonging to A and the closed half-plane associated with A which contains B.

Define two pairs (A, B), (A′, B′) to have the same orientation if $f(A, B)$ and $f(A', B')$ do. Show that this gives an equivalence relation, that there are exactly two classes, and that opposite pairs (A, B), (B, A) have opposite orientation.

5. Let X, Y, Z be three non-empty convex sets with the property that no line meets all three.

Prove that all pairs of half-lines $(D(x, y), D(x, z))$, where $x \in X$, $y \in Y$, $z \in Z$, have the same orientation.

Trigonometry

1. Elementary trigonometry

Elementary trigonometry is essentially a question of defining the trigonometric ratios properly, obtaining the addition formulas and deriving a few other relations between lengths and angles.

72. THE COSINE AND SINE OF AN ANGLE RELATIVE TO A GIVEN BASIS

Definition 72.1. Let (a, b) be an orthonormal basis for $(\Pi, 0)$ and let f be the rotation about 0 through an angle α.

The coordinates of $f(a)$ relative to this basis are called the cosine *of α and the* sine *of α (written* cos α and sin α).

First, we must see how cos α and sin α depend on the choice of basis.

Proposition 72.2. Cos α is independent of the orthonormal basis chosen. Sin α, however, changes sign for orthonormal bases of opposite orientation.

Proof. 1. If the basis (a, b) of $(\Pi, 0)$ is replaced by (b, a), $f(a)$ has coordinates cos α and $-\sin \alpha$.

2. If the basis (a', b') is obtained from (a, b) by a rotation g about 0, because $f(a) = (\cos \alpha)a + (\sin \alpha)b$,

$$f(g(a)) = g(f(a)) = (\cos \alpha)\, g(a) + (\sin \alpha)\, g(b) = (\cos \alpha)\, a' + (\sin \alpha)\, b'.$$

In other words cos α and sin α retain the same values.

3. If (a', b') is obtained from (a, b) by translation, then clearly the values remain the same because translations preserve distances and angles.

The general result comes from these three cases, because we can pass from our original orthonormal basis to any other by first taking some rotation about 0, following with a translation, and finally taking a symmetry about a line if necessary.

So whenever a configuration in plane geometry requires the sine, we must be clear which orthonormal basis we are taking. Working on the blackboard, we generally take

$\Delta(0, a)$ to be a horizontal line pointing to the right and $\Delta(0, b)$ to be pointing vertically upwards. This fits in conveniently with our intuition.

Proposition 72.3. If (A, B) *is an ordered pair of half-lines whose origins are the same,* $\cos(\widehat{AB})$ *is equal to the projection ratio* $c(A, B)$.

Proof. Let 0 be the origin, and let a be the point on A defined by $d(0, a) = 1$.

Writing f for the rotation about 0 through $\widehat{AB}$, we see that $f(a)$ is the point on B defined by $d(0, f(a)) = 1$.

Thus, if a_1 is the orthogonal projection of $f(a)$ on the line containing A, it follows from the definitions that $\cos(\widehat{AB}) = k$, where k is the scalar such that $a_1 = ka = c(A, B)$.

73. Matrix of a rotation relative to a positive orthonormal basis

Take (a, b) to be an orthonormal basis of $(\Pi, 0)$ with the same orientation as the basis of reference. Let f be the rotation about 0 through an angle α and let g be the rotation about 0 taking a to b.

Now g^2 is the symmetry with centre 0. Hence,

$$g(a) = b \qquad g(b) = g^2(a) = -a$$

Thus, from

$$(1) \qquad\qquad f(a) = (\cos \alpha)a + (\sin \alpha)b$$

we get

$$f(b) = g(f(a)) = (\cos \alpha)g(a) + (\sin \alpha)g(b), \quad \text{i.e.}$$

$$(2) \qquad\qquad f(b) = (\cos \alpha)b - (\sin \alpha)a$$

Let ξ, η be the coordinates of a point x with respect to the basis (a, b). Then $x = \xi a + \eta b$, and by (1) and (2), we get

$$f(x) = \xi f(a) + \eta f(b) = (\xi \cos \alpha - \eta \sin \alpha)a + (\xi \sin \alpha + \eta \cos \alpha)b$$

The matrix of f relative to the basis (a, b) is therefore

$$\begin{pmatrix} \cos \alpha & -\sin \alpha \\ \sin \alpha & \cos \alpha \end{pmatrix}$$

It is an easy exercise to verify that this is indeed the matrix of an isometry and, what is more, it has determinant $+1$.

Remarks. 1. Let (a, b) be an orthonormal basis of $(\Pi, 0)$ with negative orientation. Relative to this basis, the cosine and sine of α are $\cos \alpha$ and $-\sin \alpha$, giving a matrix

$$\begin{pmatrix} \cos \alpha & \sin \alpha \\ -\sin \alpha & \cos \alpha \end{pmatrix}$$

2. Any odd isometry preserving 0 can be obtained by composing some rotation about 0 with the symmetry whose axis is $\Delta(0, a)$. Its matrix therefore takes the form

$$\begin{pmatrix} \cos \alpha & \sin \alpha \\ \sin \alpha & -\cos \alpha \end{pmatrix}$$

It is easily verified that its determinant is -1, and that it has a line of fixed points.

74. ADDITION FORMULAS

Let f be a rotation about 0 through an angle α and let g be a rotation about 0 through an angle β. Their product $f \circ g = g \circ f$ is the rotation about 0 whose angle is $(\alpha + \beta)$.

Now whatever basis is chosen, the matrix of $(f \circ g)$ is the product of the matrix of f and the matrix of g. In particular, if we choose an orthonormal basis (positively or negatively orientated), we obtain the identities

(3) $\cos (\alpha + \beta) = \cos \alpha \cos \beta - \sin \alpha \sin \beta$

(4) $\sin (\alpha + \beta) = \sin \alpha \cos \beta + \cos \alpha \sin \beta$

Writing $E(\theta)$ for $\cos \theta + i \sin \theta$, for every angle θ, (3) and (4) can be combined to give the extremely useful identity

(5) $E(\alpha + \beta) = E(\alpha) \, E(\beta)$

Conversely, (5) implies (3) and (4), so it is entirely equivalent to them.

If we identify the complex plane and $(\Pi, 0)$ by identifying $(\xi + i\eta)$ with $\xi a + \eta b$, $E(\theta)$ becomes the point $f(a)$, where f is the rotation about 0 through θ. Thus E gives an injective mapping from the set $\mathscr{A}$ of angles onto the set T of complex numbers with absolute value 1. Relation (5) shows that E is not only a mapping but also an algebraic isomorphism from the additive group $\mathscr{A}$ onto the multiplicative group T.

This isomorphism is valuable. Starting with the topology of T induced by the plane topology, it enables us to define a topology on $\mathscr{A}$. This resulting topology is independent of the reference base (a, b) chosen because we can pass from one such base to another by an isometry, and this isometry is a homeomorphism because it preserves distances.

Consequences

Elementary trigonometry is now very straightforward.

From (5), we have $E(n\alpha) = (E(\alpha))^n$, and this gives the multiplication formulas of De Moivre.

Tan α can be defined and the appropriate formulas derived. We can also show that the "angle" between two lines is characterized by its tangent.

We have already derived the cosine rule

$$\alpha^2 = \beta^2 + \gamma^2 - 2\beta\gamma \cos \widehat{A}$$

The sine rule

$$\frac{\alpha}{\sin \widehat{A}} = \frac{\beta}{\sin \widehat{B}} = \frac{\gamma}{\sin \widehat{C}}$$

presents little difficulty providing we remember that the sines of any two angles (not 0 or $\bar{\omega}$) with the same orientation have the same sign.

2. Measuring angles

75. IN SEARCH OF A DEFINITION

We begin by examining the ideas underlying the measurement of simple quantities such as areas, volumes, masses, etc.

The general situation involves a set E and a family $\mathscr{E}$ of subsets of E closed under finite unions (i.e. $X_1, X_2 \in \mathscr{E} \Rightarrow X_1 \cup X_2 \in \mathscr{E}$). A measure on $\mathscr{E}$ is a mapping $X \to m(X)$ from $\mathscr{E}$ into R_+ such that $m(X_1 \cup X_2) = m(X_1) + m(X_2)$ whenever X_1, X_2 are disjoint or "almost disjoint" in some sense that is specified for each individual case. For example, if E is our plane Π and $\mathscr{E}$ is the set of finite unions of closed triangles, X_1, X_2 are almost disjoint if $X_1 \cap X_2$ is a finite union of intervals and points; in this way, area becomes a measure in the above sense.

Thus, the basic ingredients consist of a family $\mathscr{E}$ of subsets of a set E, closed under finite unions and a function m.

If we identify the group $\mathscr{A}$ of angles with the circle T of C, we can, in fact, define a particular measure on $\mathscr{A}$, of total measure 1, called the Haar measure, which is invariant under the group multiplication. This has something in common with what we call the "measurement of angles" and it is because of this that there is often a certain amount of confusion involved when measurement of angles is taught.

What we are looking for is not a set function at all, because the sum of two angles can never be thought of as the union of any two sets. Nor can we define our measure as a homomorphism from the group $\mathscr{A}$ into the additive group R (i.e. a numerical function f such that $f(\alpha + \beta) = f(\alpha) + f(\beta)$), because for a right angle δ, this gives

$$4f(\delta) = f(4\delta) = f(0) = 0$$

which will not do at all.

The proper thing is to approach matters the other way round and consider "measurement of angles" as a homomorphism of R onto the group $\mathscr{A}$. To prevent the whole thing from being far too abstract, we begin by constructing a concrete model of $\mathscr{A}$.

Let C_r be the circle with centre 0 and radius r, and let ω be an arbitrary point of C_r. For every angle α, let $\varphi(\alpha)$ be the point x of C_r such that $\widehat{\omega 0 x} = \alpha$. The mapping $\alpha \to \varphi(x)$ is injective from $\mathscr{A}$ onto C_r and it induces a group structure on C_r, isomorphic to $\mathscr{A}$ under φ, with identity element ω.

The measuring of angles will, quite simply, be the mathematical formulation of the operation of rolling a wire (representing R) on C_r in such a way that the origin of R comes into contact with the element ω of C_r.

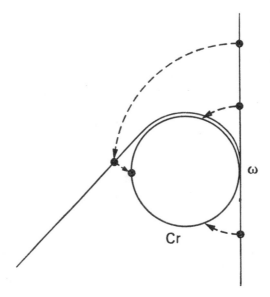

There can be no question of this operation being unique because for one thing, the radius *r* is arbitrary, and, for another, the wire can be wound in two ways giving different orientations.

76. Definition and immediate consequences

Definition 76.1. An angular measure *is a continuous mapping φ from R onto the additive group of angles $\mathscr{A}$, such that, for all $x, y \in$ R,*

$$(1) \qquad\qquad \varphi(x + y) = \varphi(x) + \varphi(y)$$

The continuity in question is relative to the topology of $\mathscr{A}$ defined by the isomorphism between $\mathscr{A}$ and the multiplicative group T of complex numbers.

From the relation (1), it follows that this continuity requirement is equivalent to the condition:

$$\varphi(x) \to 0 \quad \text{as} \quad x \to 0$$

If *k* is any non-zero number, the map $x \to kx$ is a continuous isomorphism of R onto itself. It follows that the mapping $x \to \varphi(kx)$ is also a continuous homomorphism from R onto $\mathscr{A}$, and therefore another angular measure. Thus the existence of one such angular measure implies the existence of infinitely many.

As far as teaching elementary geometry is concerned, the best thing to do is to state categorically that such a homomorphism φ exists and the only others that can exist are those that we obtained from φ in the above way.

There is no elementary proof of this fact and intellectual honesty demands that it is

therefore stated explicitly without any pretence at proof. Illustrations such as "winding a wire on a circle" will do for giving some semblance of plausibility, but no more.

Properties of such a measure φ

If φ is a continuous homomorphism from R onto $\mathscr{A}$, $\varphi^{-1}(0)$ is a closed subgroup of R. Now there exists an $x \neq 0$ such that $\varphi(x) = \bar{\omega}$, giving $\varphi(2x) = 0$. As $\varphi^{-1}(0)$ is therefore neither R nor $\{0\}$, it must be the set of multiples $\{na\}$ $(n \in Z)$ of some number $a > 0$, called the *period of φ*.

Now, for every $x \in R$, and every $n \in Z$,

$$\varphi(x + na) = \varphi(x) + \varphi(na) = \varphi(x)$$

Thus, the angle $\varphi(a/2)$ has 0 as its double, and it is therefore, either 0 or $\bar{\omega}$. But it must be $\bar{\omega}$ because $a/2$ is not a multiple of a.

Consequently, twice the angle $\varphi(a/4)$ is $\bar{\omega}$, showing that $\varphi(a/4)$ is a right angle.

If the reference basis has been chosen as an orthonormal basis for Π, we say that φ is positive if $\varphi(a/4)$ is the positive right angle. If φ is not positive, then $-\varphi$ is.

For every number $b > 0$, there exists a unique positive measure ψ of period b. For if φ is some given positive measure, of period a, ψ is the map

$$x \to \varphi\left(\frac{a}{b}x\right)$$

Depending on whether $a = 360$ or 2π (length of a unit circle), we say that the measure φ is in degrees or radians.

For every angle α_0, the equation $\varphi(x) = \alpha_0$ has at least one solution because $\varphi(R) = \mathscr{A}$. Taking x_0 as one of these, this equation becomes $\varphi(x - x_0) = 0$, showing that its solutions are the numbers $x = x_0 + na$ (where $n \in Z$). Each of these is called a measure of α_0, the one which belongs to $[0, a)$ sometimes being called the principal measure.

Every relation $\alpha_1 = \alpha_2$ in $\mathscr{A}$ can now be interpreted as meaning $x_1 - x_2 =$ multiple of a, where x_i denotes any measure of α_i $(i = 1, 2)$.

Application. Let $\alpha_0 \in \mathscr{A}$ and $p \in Z$. The relation $p\alpha = \alpha_0$ in $\mathscr{A}$ is equivalent to

$$px = x_0 + na \quad \text{where } x, x_0 \text{ are arbitrary measures of } \alpha, \alpha_0.$$

Thus

$$\alpha = \varphi\left(\frac{x_0}{p} + \frac{na}{p}\right) = \varphi\left(\frac{x_0}{p}\right) + \varphi\left(\frac{na}{p}\right)$$

and there are p distinct solutions, given by $n = 0, 1, \ldots, (p - 1)$.

77. SKETCH-PROOF OF THE EXISTENCE OF CONTINUOUS HOMOMORPHISMS FROM R ONTO T

There exist various proofs of the existence of continuous homomorphisms of R onto the multiplicative group T of complex numbers with absolute value 1. One such is sketched below.

For every complex number z, the series $\sum\limits_{0}^{\infty} \dfrac{z^n}{n!}$ is absolutely convergent. Let $f(z)$ be its sum. This is a continuous function of z (convergence in any disc; hence uniform convergence).

Next verify (product of absolutely convergent series) the identity

$$f(u + v) = f(u)\, f(v)$$

As $f(\bar{z}) = \overline{f(z)}$ (where $\overline{x + iy} = x - iy$), it follows in particular that for every $y \in \mathbf{R}$

$$f(iy)\overline{f(iy)} = f(iy)f(-iy) = f(0) = 1$$

giving $\,|\, f(iy)\,| = 1$.

Thus, the mapping φ defined by $y \to f(iy)$ is a continuous homomorphism from $\mathbf{R}$ into $\mathbf{T}$.

To show that $\varphi(\mathbf{R}) = \mathbf{T}$, put

$$\varphi(y) = c(y) + is(y) \quad (c(y) \text{ and } s(y) \text{ real})$$

The functions c and s are differentiable (differentiability of series) and we have

$$c' = -s, \; s' = c$$

From these, and the relation $c(0) = 1$, we easily deduce (properties of continuous functions) that there exists a number $l > 0$ such that

$$c(l) = 0 \quad \text{and} \quad c, s \geqslant 0 \quad \text{in } [0, l]$$

Hence, $s(l) = 1$, $\varphi(l) = i$, and $\varphi([0, l])$ is the set of elements of $\mathbf{T}$ with positive real and imaginary parts. It now readily follows that $\varphi([0, 4l]) = \mathbf{T}$, and $4l = $ period of φ.

The length of the arc $\varphi([0, l])$ of $\mathbf{T}$ is easily calculated. In fact, as $c'^2 + s'^2 = s^2 + c^2 = 1$, its length is l.

Classically, this length is denoted by $\pi/2$ (π can be accurately calculated by means of Méchain's formula, using the expansion in series for arc tan x).

Uniqueness. Showing that all continuous homomorphisms of $\mathbf{R}$ onto $\mathbf{T}$ are derived from one another by composition with some automorphism $x \to kx$ of $\mathbf{R}$, is equivalent to showing that if ψ is such a homomorphism with period 2π and with $\psi(\pi/2) = i$, then ψ is precisely the homomorphism φ that we have just considered.

To see this, we first show that the images of $[0, (\pi/2)]$ under φ and ψ are equal. But for every integer $n > 0$, $\psi(\pi/2^n) = \varphi(\pi/2^n)$, and so φ and ψ coincide on the set of numbers $p\pi/2^n$. This is a dense subset of $\mathbf{R}$ and the continuity of φ and ψ now gives the result.

Remarks. 1. In analysis, the functions c and s are called cosine and sine; this terminology is justified by the fact that $s(t)$ is the sine of the angle associated with $\varphi(t)$. This is a convenient convention, but we must remember that it presupposes that the angular measure adopted is positive and made in radians.

2. When teaching elementary analysis, the mapping $t \to \sin(\varphi(t))$ is proved to be differentiable for angular measures φ by "showing", rather than proving, that when φ is positive and in radians, $\lim\limits_{t \to 0} \sin(\varphi(t))/t = 1$.

It is more honest to state explicitly that we are assuming the existence of some φ satisfying this relation, and then prove for such φ that $dx^2 + dy^2 = dt^2$. This last relation can then be given an intuitive interpretation such as rolling R on T.

78. ARITHMETICAL MEASURE OF AN ANGLE

Definition 78.1. *Take φ as angular measure in radians. For every angle α, the* arithmetic measure OF α *(in radians) is defined as* $p(\alpha) = \inf\{|x| : \varphi(x) = \alpha\}$

Clearly $p(\alpha) = p(-\alpha)$ because $\varphi(-x) = -\varphi(x)$.
Let us show that $p(\alpha + \beta) \leqslant p(\alpha) + p(\beta)$.
Now there exists $x \in R$ such that $\varphi(x) = \alpha$ and $|x| = p(\alpha)$, and there exists $y \in R$ such that $\varphi(y) = \beta$ and $|y| = p(\beta)$.
But $\varphi(x + y) = \alpha + \beta$ and so

$$p(\alpha + \beta) \leqslant |x + y| \leqslant |x| + |y| = p(\alpha) + p(\beta)$$

Thus, for $\alpha, \beta \in \mathscr{A}$, if we put

$$d(\alpha, \beta) = p(\beta - \alpha)$$

we obtain a distance function on $\mathscr{A}$ invariant under the group operation.
We can also obtain a distance function on the set of directions of half-lines by putting $d(A, B) = p(\widehat{AB})$.

Remark. Every angle $\alpha \neq \bar{\omega}$ is characterized by its arithmetical measure and its orientation; this explains why it is possible to develop a theory for angles starting from this. However, mere possibility is no justification for carrying out such an approach.

Exercises on Chapter VII

1. Let f be a continuous mapping of $[a, b]$ into the group $T = R/Z$, such that $f(a) = 0$. Let φ be the canonical mapping from R onto T.
   Show that there exists a unique continuous map g of $[a, b]$ into R such that $g(a) = 0$ and $f = \varphi \circ g$.

2. Let (α_i) be an arbitrary finite family of angles with the same orientation. Denoting the arithmetic measure of an angle by p, show that

$$(\textstyle\sum p(\alpha_i) \leqslant \pi) \Rightarrow (p(\textstyle\sum \alpha_i) = \textstyle\sum p(\alpha_i))$$

3. Show that for every triangle (a, b, c) with distinct vertices, the sum of the arithmetic measures of the angles of the triangle is equal to π.

The circle

79. DEFINITION AND SYMMETRIES OF A CIRCLE

Definition 79.1. Let $a \in \Pi$, and let ρ be a positive number.
  The subset of Π defined by $d(a, x) = \rho$ is called the circle of radius ρ and centre a.
  The subset defined by $d(a, x) < \rho$ is called the interior of the circle.
  The subset defined by $d(a, x) > \rho$ is called the exterior of the circle.
  The circle is denoted by $C(a, \rho)$ and the interior by $D(a, \rho)$. The sets $D(a, \rho)$, $D(a, \rho) \cup C(a, \rho)$ are also called the *open* and *closed discs* of radius ρ and centre a respectively.
  Trivially, every half-line originating at a meets $C(a, \rho)$ in a unique point. Moreover a is a centre of symmetry for $C(a, \rho)$.

Proposition 79.2. 1. The point a is the unique centre of symmetry of $C(a, \rho)$.
2. The only axes of symmetry of $C(a, \rho)$ are the lines passing through a.

Proof. 1. Let a' be a centre of symmetry of $C(a, \rho)$, and let D be a line containing a and a'. D meets $C(a, \rho)$ in two points, and a, a' are both midpoints of these. Hence $a = a'$.

2. Let D be a line passing through a, and let φ be the symmetry whose axis is D. Now,

$$(x \in C(a, \rho) \Rightarrow (d(a, \varphi(x)) = d(a, x) = \rho) \Rightarrow (\varphi(x) \in C(a, \rho))$$

Thus $\varphi(C(a, \rho)) \subset C(a, \rho)$, and it follows that

$$C(a, \rho) = \varphi^2(C(a, \rho)) \subset \varphi(C(a, \rho))$$

Hence $\varphi(C(a, \rho)) = C(a, \rho)$; in other words, D is an axis of symmetry for $C(a, \rho)$.
  Conversely, suppose D is an axis of symmetry of $C(a, \rho)$ and let D' be the perpendicular to D passing through a. D and D' are two perpendicular axes of symmetry and their intersection is consequently a centre of symmetry of $C(a, \rho)$. Thus it must be a, showing that D passes through a.

Corollary 79.3. $(C(a, \rho) = C(a', \rho')) \Rightarrow (a = a'$ and $\rho = \rho')$.

  For as a and a' are *centres of symmetry of the same circle* $a = a'$, and $\rho = \rho'$ readily follows.

Corollary 79.4. $C(a, \rho)$ *is stable under any rotation about its centre. More exactly, the circles* $C(a, \rho)$, *for various* ρ, *and the set* $\{a\}$ *are the orbits in* Π *under the action of the group* $\mathscr{R}_a$ *of rotations about a.*

Corollary 79.5. *If* C, C' *are a pair of circles whose centres are distinct, the line joining the centres is an axis of symmetry for* $C \cup C'$ *and* $C \cap C'$.

80. IMAGE OF A CIRCLE UNDER A SIMILITUDE

Proposition 80.1. *The transform of the circle* $C(a, \rho)$ *by a similitude f of proportionality ratio k* $(k > 0)$ *is the circle* $C(f(a), k\rho)$.

Proof. The implication

$$(1) \qquad\qquad f(C(a, \rho)) \subset C(f(a), k\rho)$$

is obvious. As the inverse f^{-1} of f is a similitude of ratio k^{-1}, so is the implication

$$(2) \qquad\qquad f^{-1}(C(f(a), k\rho) \subset C(a, \rho)$$

Applying f to both sides of the inclusion (2),

$$(3) \qquad\qquad C(f(a), k\rho) \subset f(C(a, \rho))$$

and, comparing (1) and (3), the proposition follows.

Proposition 80.2. *For every pair of circles* $C(a, \rho)$, $C(a', \rho')$, *there exist exactly two distinct dilations of* Π *which transform the first into the second. Their ratios are equal in magnitude but opposite in sign.*

Proof. In the pointed plane $(\Pi, 0)$, the transform of $C(a, \rho)$ by the dilation $x \to hx + b$ $(h \in R^*, b \in (\Pi, 0))$ is the circle with centre $ha + b$ and radius $|h|\rho$ (Prop. 80.1).

For this circle to coincide with $C(a', \rho')$, we need

$$a' = ha + b \quad \text{and} \quad \rho' = |h|\rho$$

Thus,

$$h = \pm\rho'/\rho, \qquad b = a' - ha,$$

and from these equations, the required dilations can be determined explicitly. They must be distinct because their ratios are opposite.

Particular cases

1. $\rho = \rho'$. One of the dilations is the translation $x \to x + (a' - a)$, the other is the symmetry whose centre is the midpoint of (a, a').
2. $a = a'$. The dilations are both homothetic transformations with centre $a = a'$.
3. If $\rho \neq \rho'$ and $a \neq a'$, the two dilations are homothetic transformations. Their centres are obviously on $\Delta(a, a')$ and divide (a, a') in the ratios ρ/ρ' and $-\rho/\rho'$. They are therefore harmonic conjugates with respect to (a, a').

81. CONVEXITY OF DISCS

Proposition 81.1. Every open (or closed) disc is convex.

Proof. Let $b, c \in D(a, \rho)$, then

$$(x \in [b, c]) \Rightarrow (d(a, x) \leqslant \sup (d(a, b), d(a, c)) \quad \text{(see Corollary 40.4)}$$

Hence $d(a, x) < \rho$.

The same reasoning applies to a closed disc.

Corollary. The intersection of two discs (called a lune) is convex. The intersection of a disc and a half plane is convex.

82. INTERSECTION OF A CIRCLE AND A LINE

Proposition 82.1. Let D be a line, C a circle of radius ρ and centre a, and d the distance between a and D. Let D' be the perpendicular to D passing through a, x_0 the point of intersection of D and D'. Then,

$$(d > \rho) \Rightarrow (D \cap C = \varnothing) \quad \text{and} \quad D \subset \text{exterior of } C$$

$$(d = \rho) \Rightarrow (D \cap C = x_0) \quad \text{and} \quad D - \{x_0\} \subset \text{exterior of } C$$

$$(d < \rho) \Rightarrow (D \cap C = \{x_1, x_2\} \text{ where } x_1 \neq x_2 \text{ and } \begin{cases} (x_1, x_2) \subset \text{interior of } C \\ D - [x_1, x_2] \subset \text{exterior of } C \end{cases}$$

This is an easy consequence of Prop. 40.1.

Corollary 82.2. If u is in the interior of C and v is in the exterior of C, then $[u, v]$ meets C in a unique point.

If D is the line containing u, v, it is clear that we have case 3 of the above proposition. Hence, $u \in (x_1, x_2)$ and $v \in D - [x_1, x_2]$. The corollary now follows.

Application. If $u_1, u_2, \ldots, u_n \in \Pi$, with u_1 in the interior of C and u_n in the exterior, then one of the intervals $[u_i, u_{i+1}]$ meets C. For, if p is the largest index i such that u_i is in the interior of C, then $p \neq n$, and u_{p+1} is in the exterior of C. As above, $[u_p, u_{p+1}]$ meets C.

83. TANGENT TO A CIRCLE

Definition 83.1. The tangent to the circle $C(a, \rho)$ at the point x on the circle is defined as the line D passing through x perpendicular to $\Delta(x, a)$.

Proposition 82.1 shows that D meets the circle at x_0 only, and that $(D - \{x\})$ is in the exterior of the circle. It follows that no tangent passes through any interior point of the circle, and the only tangent which passes through a point x on the circle is the tangent at this point.

The following equivalences obviously hold:

(D is the tangent to C at x)

$$\Leftrightarrow (D \cap C = \{x\})$$

$$\Leftrightarrow (\text{the projection of } a \text{ on D is } x \text{ and } d(a, x) = \rho)$$

Proposition 83.2. If f is a similitude of Π, *and* C *is a circle, then*

$$(\text{D is a tangent to C at } x) \Leftrightarrow (f(\text{D}) \text{ is a tangent to } f(\text{C}) \text{ at } f(x))$$

Proof. This is true because, for example, the two statements can be translated into

$$(\text{D} \cap \text{C}) = \{x\} \quad \text{and} \quad f(\text{D}) \cap f(\text{C}) = \{f(x)\}$$

In particular, if f is a dilation, the tangents to C and $f(\text{C})$ at corresponding points are parallel.

84. INTERSECTION OF TWO CIRCLES

Let $C(a, \rho)$ and $C(a', \rho')$ be two circles. If they have a point x in common, the triplet (a, a', x) has sides of length $d(a, a')$, ρ, ρ'.

Conversely, if there exists a plane triangle (b, b', y) with sides $d(a, a')$, ρ, ρ' there is an isometry f which takes (b, b') to (a, a'), and the point $f(y)$ belongs to both circles.

Applying one of the criteria for the existence of a plane triangle with the given sides, we can state:

Proposition 84.1. Let C, C' *be two circles, of radii* ρ, ρ', *whose centres are distance* d *apart. Then,*

$$(\text{C} \cap \text{C}' \neq \varnothing) \Leftrightarrow (|\rho - \rho'| \leqslant d \leqslant \rho + \rho')$$

The significance of this proposition lies in the following remarks:

When $d = 0$, the condition gives $\rho = \rho'$, i.e. $\text{C} \cap \text{C}' = \text{C} = \text{C}'$.
When $d \neq 0$, but both inequalities are strict, $\text{C}_1 \cap \text{C}_2 = \{x_1, x_2\}$

where x_1, x_2 are distinct points placed symmetrically about the line of centres.

When $d \neq 0$, and one inequality becomes equality, the points x_1, x_2 coincide and the circles have a common tangent at this point (in this case, we say that the circles are tangential).

85. EQUATION OF A CIRCLE

Let (u_1, u_2) be an orthonormal basis for the plane $(\Pi, 0)$ and let x_1, x_2 denote the co-ordinates of the point x relative to this basis.

Proposition 85.1. $(x \in C(a, \rho)) \Leftrightarrow ((x_1 - a_1)^2 + (x_2 - a_2)^2 = \rho^2)$.

Proof. This follows simply because the condition $x \in C(a, \rho)$ is equivalent to the condition $d^2(a, x) = \rho^2$.

The relation $(x_1 - a_1)^2 + (x_2 - a_2)^2 = \rho^2$ has the form

$$x_1^2 + x_2^2 + 2\alpha x_1 + 2\beta x_2 + \gamma = 0$$

Let us examine the question of when such an equation is the equation of the circle. First, we rewrite the equation as

$$(x_1 + \alpha)^2 + (x_2 + \beta)^2 + \gamma - \alpha^2 + \beta^2 = 0$$

We now see that:

if $\gamma > \alpha^2 + \beta^2$, the left-hand side is strictly positive and no solution is possible;

if $\gamma = \alpha^2 + \beta^2$, the only solution is the point $(-\alpha, -\beta)$;

if $\gamma > \alpha^2 + \beta^2$, a solution is possible and it is the circle with centre $(-\alpha, -\beta)$ with radius $\rho = (\alpha^2 + \beta^2 - \gamma)^{\frac{1}{2}}$.

To say that $C(a, \rho)$ passes through 0 is the same as saying that $a_1^2 + a_2^2 = \rho^2$, or $\gamma = 0$.

86. SOME CHARACTERISTIC PROPERTIES OF THE CIRCLE

Without exaggerating their importance, let us list a few classical properties; most of them ought to have no more status than that accorded to an exercise.

1. Let $a, b \in \Pi$, with mid-point 0.
If $x \in C(0, \rho)$,

$$d^2(x, a) + d^2(x, b) = 2\rho^2 + 2d^2(0, a)$$

Conversely, for every $k > 2d^2(0, a)$, the set of points $x \in \Pi$ such that $d^2(x, a) + d^2(x, b) = k$ is a circle with centre 0.

2. Take $a, b \in \Pi$ (with $a \neq b$), and let k be a positive number. Let E be the set of elements x of Π such that $d(x, a) = kd(x, b)$.

The determination of E by so-called "elementary" methods is fairly tricky. So here we have a splendid opportunity for demonstrating the power and uniformity of algebraic methods.

Choose an orthonormal basis in which the first axis is $\Delta(a, b)$. The original relation can be written as

$$d^2(x, a) - k^2 d^2(x, b) = 0 \quad \text{or} \quad (x_1 - a_1)^2 + x_2^2 - k^2((x_1 - b_1)^2 + x_2^2) = 0$$

If $k = 1$, E is clearly the perpendicular bisector of (a, b).
If $k \neq 1$, this equation is evidently of the form

$$x_1^2 + x_2^2 + 2\alpha x_1 + 2\beta x_2 + \gamma = 0 \quad \text{after division by } (1 - k^2)$$

As E has two distinct points m_1, m_2 on $\Delta(a, b)$, the statements which follow Prop. 85.1 show that E is a circle. As $\Delta(a, b)$ is an axis of symmetry of E, it must be a circle with diameter (m_1, m_2). Notice that (m_1, m_2) divides (a, b) harmonically.

Conversely, if C is a circle and a, b are two points on an axis of symmetry D such that the pair (a, b) divides the points m_1, m_2 of $C \cap D$ harmonically, the set of points x such that

$$d(x, a) = kd(x, b) \quad \text{where} \quad k = \frac{d(m_1, a)}{d(m_1, b)} = \frac{d(m_2, a)}{d(m_2, b)}$$

is precisely C.

3. Usually, a fair amount of attention is devoted to theorems about angles subtended by a chord at points on a circle, a careful distinction being made between the angle between a pair of lines and the angle between a pair of half-lines. We shall show that,

by appropriate reformulation, angles between lines can be avoided and a very simple treatment obtained.

Lemma 86.1. *Let $(x, 0, y)$ be an isosceles triplet $(d(0, x) = d(0, y))$ of distinct vertices. Then*

$$\widehat{x0y} + 2\widehat{0yx} = \widehat{x0y} + 2\widehat{yx0} = \bar{\omega}$$

Proof. By Corollary 59.2,

$$\widehat{x0y} + \widehat{0yx} + \widehat{yx0} = \bar{\omega} \quad \text{and} \quad \widehat{0yx} = \widehat{yx0}$$

Proposition 86.2. *If (a, x, b) is a non-collinear triplet of points of Π, then $2\widehat{axb} = \widehat{a0b}$, where 0 denotes the centre of the circle passing through a, b, x.*

Proof. Applying Lemma 86.1 to the isosceles triangles $(x, 0, a)$ and $(b, 0, x)$, we have:

$$\widehat{x0a} + 2\widehat{a0x} = \bar{\omega} \quad \text{and} \quad \widehat{b0x} + 2\widehat{x0b} = \bar{\omega}$$

Adding,

$$\widehat{b0a} + 2\widehat{axb} = 0 \quad \text{or} \quad 2\widehat{axb} = \widehat{a0b}$$

Corollary 86.3. *Let a, b be distinct points of Π, and let α be a non-zero angle. Let C be the circle passing through a, b whose centre 0 is defined by*

$$2\widehat{ba0} = \bar{\omega} - \alpha$$

Then, for every x distinct from a and b,

$$(x \in C) \Leftrightarrow (2\widehat{axb} = \alpha)$$

Proof. Whenever 0 is a point on the perpendicular bisector of (a, b), the relation $2\widehat{ba0} = \bar{\omega} - \alpha$ is equivalent to $\widehat{a0b} = \alpha$.

On the other hand, if a, x, b are collinear, then

$$2\widehat{axb} = 0 \neq \alpha$$

Now let $x \in \Pi$, with $x \neq a$ and $x \neq b$.

If $x \in C$, Prop. 86.2 shows that $2\widehat{axb} = \widehat{a0b} = \alpha$.

Conversely, if $2\widehat{axb} = \alpha$, the points a, x, b are not collinear, and if $0'$ denotes the centre of the circle passing through a, x, b, the same proposition gives $a0'b = \alpha$, i.e. $0 = 0'$, $x \in C$.

Remark. Let β_1, β_2 be the two solutions of $2\beta_i = \alpha$. Then we have $\beta_i \neq 0$ or $\bar{\omega}(i = 1, 2)$ and $\beta_1 - \beta_2 = \bar{\omega}$. Thus one of these angles has positive orientation, the other negative.

Now the orientation of $\widehat{axb}$ is positive or negative depending on whether x is in one or other of the open half-planes Π_1, Π_2 associated with $\Delta(a, b)$ (the orientation being that of $\widehat{xba}$ by Prop. 69.1).

Thus, on one of the arcs $C \cap \Pi_1$, $\overset{\frown}{axb}$ takes the value β_1, and on the other β_2. It follows from this that for every angle β, the set of points x of Π such that

$$\overset{\frown}{axb} = \beta$$

is a circular arc with extremities at a and b.

87. THE POWER OF A POINT WITH RESPECT TO A CIRCLE

Definition 87.1. The power of a point x of Π with respect to a circle $C(a, \rho)$ is defined as the number $P(x) = d^2(a, x) - \rho^2$. The function $x \to P(x)$ is referred to as the power map with respect to $C(a, \rho)$.

Clearly, $P(x) < 0$, $P(x) > 0$, or $P(x) = 0$ depending on whether x is interior to, exterior to, or on the circle.

With any orthonormal basis,

$$P(x) = (x_1 - a_1)^2 + (x_2 - a_2)^2 - \rho^2$$

Proposition 87.2. Let P be the power map with respect to a circle C, and let $x \in \Pi$.

1. *If p, q is a pair of diametrically opposite points of C, then*

$$P(x) = \overrightarrow{xp} \cdot \overrightarrow{xq}$$

2. *If p, p' are a pair of distinct points of C collinear with x, then*

$$P(x) = \overrightarrow{xp} \cdot \overrightarrow{xp'} = \overrightarrow{xp} \times \overrightarrow{xp'}$$

3. *If x is on the tangent to C at a point p,*

$$P(x) = (\overrightarrow{xp})^2 = d^2(x, p)$$

Proof. Let a be the centre of C, and ρ its radius.

1. $\overrightarrow{xp} \cdot \overrightarrow{xq} = (\overrightarrow{xa} + \overrightarrow{ap}) \cdot (\overrightarrow{xa} - \overrightarrow{ap}) = \overrightarrow{xa}^2 - \overrightarrow{ap}^2 = d^2(a, x) - \rho^2 = P(x)$

2. Let q be the point symmetric to p with respect to a. We know that $\overrightarrow{p'q}$ and $\overrightarrow{xp}$ are perpendicular and so,

$$\overrightarrow{xp} \cdot \overrightarrow{xp'} = \overrightarrow{xp} \cdot (\overrightarrow{xq} + \overrightarrow{qp'}) = \overrightarrow{xp} \cdot \overrightarrow{xq'} = P(x)$$

3. As is well known, in the right angle triangle (x, a, p)

$$d^2(x, p) = d^2(a, x) - \rho^2 = P(x)$$

Radical axis and coaxial systems

Let C, C' be a pair of distinct circles and let P, P' be the powers with respect to them. Let k be an arbitrary number.

Performing a simple calculation (relative to some suitable orthonormal basis), we determine the equation of the set of points x such that $P(x) = kP'(x)$, and compare the result obtained with the result concerning the circles given by the equation $d(x, a) = hd(x, b)$.

Exercises on Chapter VIII

1. Let X be the exterior of some circle. Show that X is connected in the sense that any two points in X can be joined by a polygonal line lying entirely in X.

2. Show that every closed disc and every open disc is the intersection of some family of open half-planes. Deduce that such discs are convex.

3. Let D be a closed circular disc in Π. Show that for every point x, there is a unique point $p(x)$ of D such that the distance $d(x, p(x))$ is a minimum. (This point $p(x)$ is called the *projection* of x on D.) Show that this projection diminishes distances (i.e. $d(p(u), p(v)) \leqslant d(u, v)$).

4. Let X be any non-empty subset of Π, r a positive constant, and δ the direction of some given line.
   Find the set of points which are points of contact of tangents with direction δ to circles $C(x, r)$, with $x \in X$.

5. Let X be any subset of Π, let $0 \in \Pi$ and let δ be the direction of some line. Let Y be the set of points which are points of contact of the tangents with direction δ to circles through 0 whose centres are in X. How is Y obtained from X?

6. Let A, B be two lines. Take $u \in A$, $v \in B$ (with $u \neq v$). For $x \in \Pi$, $x \neq u$, $x \neq v$, let $\alpha(x)$ be the circle through x tangential to A at u and $\beta(x)$ the circle through x tangential to B at v. For what points x are $\alpha(x)$ and $\beta(x)$ tangential?

7. Let f be an even similitude of Π. Let $a \in \Pi$.
   Describe the set of points x such that $x \neq f(x)$ and such that $a \in \Delta(x, f(x))$.

8. Let C, C' be two circles of different radii.
   Determine the set of even similitudes transforming C to C'. Do the same for the odd similitudes, and show that their axes pass through some fixed point.

9. Let D be a line, C a circle and k a constant.
   For each point x, let $P(x)$ denote the power of x with respect to C, and $d(x)$ its distance from D. For what points x does the equation $P(x) = kd(x)$ hold?

10. Let $(C_i)_{i \in I}$ be a finite family of circles, and let $(\lambda_i)_{i \in I}$ be a family of numbers. For each $i \in I$, let P_i denote power with respect to C_i.
   Find the set of points x such that

$$\sum \lambda_i P_i(x) = C \quad \text{(where C is some given constant)}$$

Examine the particular case where $\sum \lambda_i = 0$.
When is the function $\sum \lambda_i P_i$ constant over Π?

Space

1. Axioms

88. Choosing a method

In the Introduction, we emphasized that when plane geometry is first taught formally, the axiomatization used should be intuitive, bringing out the relationship between the physical world and that of mathematics.

After the pupil has grasped such an axiomatization and has become familiar with vectors and inner products, it is not so important that the same approach should be made to a study of space. This is especially true if he has already had sufficient experience in manipulating material to give him an intuitive knowledge of the geometry of three dimensions and, in particular, a familiarity with coordinate systems, rectangular or otherwise.

However we shall see that an axiomatization of space can be formulated which is an extension to that of the plane. Moreover, thanks to the previous study of the plane, we can rapidly establish its structure as an inner product space.

This is why we think it better to defer a systematic study of inner product spaces to the top class (17 or 18 years old). After an axiomatic study of the plane or space, this then appears as a fruitful generalization if carried out within the framework of general finite dimensional vector spaces.

Few additions are needed to the plane axiomatization to obtain axioms for space. They are essentially summarized by:

(a) Through any three points, there is at least one plane.
(b) Any plane containing two points of a line contains the whole line.
(c) The complement of a plane P can be partitioned into two non-empty sets E_1, E_2 in such a way that any interval with extremities in E_1 and E_2 must meet P.

But to understand fully what these properties involve, we need to see them in the context of the other axioms and we proceed to list these explicitly, below.

89. Axioms for three dimensional space

Space consists of a set E, a family $\mathscr{D}$ of subsets of E called *lines*, and a family $\mathscr{P}$ of subsets of E called *planes*. The lines and planes both have structures determined by certain axioms and the various structures are linked by other axioms.

We suppose that E contains at least two distinct planes, each plane contains at least two distinct lines, and each line contains at least two distinct points.

Definition 89.1. Two lines A, B *are said to be parallel* (written A ∥ B) *if either* A = B *or* A, B *are contained in a plane and do not intersect.*

I. *Axioms of incidence*

(a) For every pair (x, y) of distinct points of E, there exists one and only one line containing x and y.

(b) For every plane P, every line D ⊂ P, and every point $x \in$ P, there is one and only one line of P which passes through x and is parallel to D.

(c) Every plane containing two points of a line contains the whole line.

(d) For every triplet (x, y, z) of points, there exists at least one plane containing them.

II. *Axioms of order*

(a) Every line has two total orderings, the one the reverse of the other.

(b) If A, B are parallel lines and a, b, a', b' points such that a, $a' \in$ A, b, $b' \in$ B, then any line parallel to A and B intersecting $[a, b]$ also intersects $[a', b']$.

III. *Axioms for the additive structure*

(a) There exists a map d from E × E into R$_+$, called *distance* satisfying the following properties:

1. $d(y, x) = d(x, y)$, for all x, y.

2. If D is an orientated line, $x \in$ D, and l is a positive number, then there exists a unique point y of D such that

$$x \leqslant y \quad \text{and} \quad d(x, y) = l$$

3. $$(x \in [a, b]) \Rightarrow (d(a, x) + d(x, b) = d(a, b))$$

(b) If A, B are parallel lines and a, b, a', b' points such that a, $a' \in$ A and b, $b' \in$ B, then the line parallel to these lines through the mid-point of (a, b) also passes through the mid-point of (a', b').

IV. *Axioms for perpendiculars and symmetry*

(a) For every plane P, there exists a binary relation ⊥, called the perpendicularity relation, such that

1. (A ⊥ B) ⇔ (B ⊥ A)   (symmetry)

2. $(A \perp B) \Rightarrow$ (A and B are not parallel).

3. For every line A of P, there is at least one line B of P such that $A \perp B$.

4. If (A, B) is a pair of lines such that $(A \perp B)$, then the equivalence $(B \parallel B') \Leftrightarrow (A \perp B')$ holds for every line B' of P.

(b) If (A_1, A_2) is a pair of half-lines with the same origin, then $c(A_1, A_2) = c(A_2, A_1)$.

V. *Dimension axiom*

For every plane P, there exists a partitioning of the complement of P into two non-empty subsets E_1, E_2 such that

$$(x_1 \in E_1, x_2 \in E_2) \Rightarrow (P \cap [x_1, x_2] \text{ is non-empty}).$$

Of course, in many of these axioms, terms and notations are employed which, in any complete exposition would have to be broken down into simpler terms; for example, the notation $c(A_1, A_2)$. However, given the axiomatization of the plane that we already have there is no difficulty about their meaning.

In what follows, a pair of lines A, B are said to *intersect* if $A \neq B$ and $A \cap B \neq \varnothing$ (their intersection then has to be a single point by Axiom I(a)). A line D and a plane P intersect if $D \not\subset P$ and $D \cap P \neq \varnothing$ (in which case the intersection is again a single point by I(c)).

90. ELEMENTARY CONSEQUENCES

Notice immediately that for any plane P of E, the axioms reduce to those of plane geometry and so we can assume for P all the results proved to date.

We shall see that Axioms I, II, III, IV characterize general affine spaces which have an associated metric and an inner product, and that Axiom V only comes in at the end to show that the dimension of space is 3.

Proposition 90.1. If a, b, c is a set of non-collinear points of E, then there is a unique plane containing them.

Proof. By Axiom I(a), one such plane exists. Suppose then that P_1, P_2 are two such planes. Axiom I(c) then shows that they both contain $\Delta(a, b)$, $\Delta(a, c)$ and $\Delta(b, c)$. However, for every x of P_1 not on these lines, there exists a line through x in P_1 meeting $\Delta(a, b)$ and $\Delta(b, c)$ in distinct points y, z. As y and $z \in P_2$, it follows that $\Delta(y, z) \subset P_2$ and, therefore, $x \in P_2$. Thus $P_1 \subset P_2$ and, by a similar argument, $P_2 \subset P_1$. This gives the result.

Corollary 90.2. If a pair of lines intersect, there is a unique plane containing them.
For every line D, and every point $x \notin D$, there is a unique plane containing D and x.

Corollary 90.3. For every line D, and every point x there is a unique line parallel to D through x.

Let us just prove Corollary 90.3. This is obvious if $x \in D$ and, if not, we use the fact that there is a unique plane containing D and x, applying Axiom I(b) to this plane.

It follows from this corollary that for every line D, the relation

"$(x \sim y)$ if there is a line parallel to D containing x and y"

is an equivalence relation on E in which the classes are the lines parallel to D.

However, we do not know, at this stage, how to prove that parallelism is an equivalence relation on the set $\mathscr{D}$ of lines.

2. Affine structure of space

91. THE POINTED SPACE $(E, 0)$

Assuming that some origin for E has been chosen, we now show how E becomes a vector space over R using only Axioms I, II, III of this Chapter. In the subsequent paragraphs, the symbols $(D, 0)$, $(P, 0)$ denote the vector spaces consisting of the pointed lines and planes described in Chapter II.

Definition 91.1. For $0 \in E$, the pointed plane $(E, 0)$ consists of the set E under the binary operator $(x, y) \to x + y$ and the scalar multiplication $(\lambda, x) \to \lambda x$ defined as follows:

1. *If $0, x, y$ are not collinear, $x + y$ is the sum of x and y in the (unique) pointed plane $(P, 0)$ containing them.*

2. *If $0, x, y$ are collinear but not all coincident with 0, $x + y$ is the sum of x and y in the pointed line $(D, 0)$ which contains them.*

3. *If $x = y = 0$, $x + y = 0$.*

Finally, the multiplication $(\lambda, x) \to \lambda x$ is the scalar product of λ with x in the pointed line $(D, 0)$ containing x.

Chapter II immediately suggests the following important result:

Proposition 91.2. The pointed space $(E, 0)$ is a vector space over R. The subspaces of dimensions 1 and 2 are the lines and planes of E which pass through 0.

Proof. 1. Nearly all the axioms for a vector space are easily verified, including the relation $\lambda(x + y) = \lambda x + \lambda y$ which is true in the pointed plane $(P, 0)$ containing $0, x, y$. The only property which is not evident is that of associativity:

$$(1) \qquad (a + b) + c = a + (b + c)$$

To establish this, set

$$\gamma = \text{mid-point of } (a, b) \quad \text{and} \quad \alpha = \text{mid-point of } (b, c)$$

Then,

$$2\gamma = a + b \quad \text{and} \quad 2\alpha = b + c$$

(taking planes containing $(0, a, b)$ and $(0, b, c)$ respectively).
But relation (1) is equivalent to

$$(2) \qquad \tfrac{1}{3}(2\gamma + c) = \tfrac{1}{3}(a + 2\alpha)$$

and, for every $x, y \in \Pi$, $\tfrac{1}{3}(x + 2y)$ is the point which divides (x, y) in the ratio $k = -2$ (taking a plane containing $(0, x, y)$.

Thus, relation (2) is verified, by a well-known property of the plane triple (a, b, c) (the centre of gravity).

2. The lines of E passing through 0 are clearly the vector subspaces of dimension 1. Every plane passing through 0 has the structure of the pointed plane $(P, 0)$, which is a vector space, and so it is a subspace of E of dimension 2. Conversely, let A be a vector subspace of E of dimension 2. If (a_1, a_2) is a basis of A, the pointed plane $(P, 0)$ containing $0, a_1, a_2$ is a vector subspace of E of dimension 2, and this shows that $A = P$.

92. Translations

Definition 92.1. A mapping f of E into itself such that, for all $x, y \in E$, $(x, y, f(y), f(x))$ is a parallelogram (i.e. mid-point of $(x, f(y))$ = mid-point of $(y, f(x))$) is called a translation.

Proposition 92.2. For $a, b \in E$, there exists a unique translation transforming a to b. In every pointed plane $(E, 0)$ this translation is given as the map

$$x \to x + (b - a)$$

Proof. If there exists a translation with $b = f(a)$, then, for every x (using the operations of $(E, 0)$):

$$\tfrac{1}{2}(a + f(x)) = \tfrac{1}{2}(x + f(a)) = \tfrac{1}{2}(x + b)$$

showing that $f(x) = x + (b - a)$.

Conversely, it is clear that $f: x \to x + (b - a)$ is a translation with the required property.

Evidently the translations of E form an abelian group which acts as a simply transitive transformation group on E, and is isomorphic to the additive group $(E, 0)$ for all $0 \in E$.

Proposition 92.3. For every $a, b \in E$, let $\top$ and $\perp$ denote addition in (E, a), (E, b) respectively, and let $\wedge$ and $\vee$ denote the respective scalar multiplications in these spaces. Suppose that f is the translation transforming a to b.

Then the translation f is an isomorphism from (E, a) onto (E, b); in other words, for every $x, y \in E$, and for every scalar λ

$$f(x \top y) = f(x) \perp f(y) \quad \text{and} \quad f(\lambda \wedge x) = \lambda \vee f(x)$$

The first statement comes, for example, from the fact that $b = f(a)$ and that f transforms every parallelogram into a parallelogram.

The second is true because it is true in a plane containing $a, b, x, f(x)$.

Corollary 92.4. The translation f transforms every line (or plane) passing through a into a line (or plane) passing through b.

For f is an isomorphism of (E, a) onto (E, b) and therefore it preserves the dimension of subspaces.

93. Parallelism

Definition 93.1. Two planes P, P' of E are said to be parallel (written $P \parallel P'$) if there exists some translation which transforms P into P'.

This is a particular instance of a definition valid for a general vector space.

Proposition 93.2 $(P \parallel P') \Leftrightarrow$ *(For every $a \in P$, every $a \in P'$, the translation mapping a to a' maps P to P').*

A similar statement holds for lines.

Proof. For lines this is already established because it concerns translations in a plane. For planes, the proof is the same as that given for arbitrary affine sub-spaces of a vector space.

Corollary 93.3 Parallelism is an equivalence relation on the set $\mathscr{D}$ of lines and the set $\mathscr{P}$ of planes.

From this directions can be given to planes and lines, concretely representable by the planes and lines through the chosen origin.

Corollary 93.4. There is just one plane which passes through a given point x which has the same direction as a given plane P. (Similarly for lines.)

Definition 93.5. Let D be a line and P a plane. Let D', P' be the corresponding line and plane which are parallel to D, P and pass through 0. Then we say that D is parallel to P (and write D | P) if $D' \subset P'$.

Obviously this definition is independent of the choice of origin. The parallelism so defined is a binary relation between $\mathscr{D}$ and $\mathscr{P}$ but care should be taken not to confuse it with an equivalence relation. For example, (D | P and D | P') does not imply $(P \parallel P')$, neither does (D | P and D' | P) imply $(D \parallel D')$. However, it is true, and follows from the definition, that

$$(D \mid P, D \parallel D', P \parallel P') \Rightarrow (D' \mid P')$$

Furthermore, for any point x, the lines through x parallel to a plane P generate the plane P' which is parallel to P and passes through x. Similarly, for $x \in E$, the intersection of planes through x which are parallel to a given line D is that line D' through x parallel to D.

94. CONSEQUENCES OF THE DIMENSION AXIOM

The time has come to use Axiom V and obtain the dimension of E. However, we shall not make any use of this result when studying the metric properties of space so that anything proved there will hold for all affine spaces.

Proposition 94.1. If Axioms I, II, III are all satisfied, then Axiom V is equivalent to each of the following properties:

(α) *If P, Q are distinct planes, either $P \cap Q = \varnothing$ or $P \cap Q$ is a line.*

(β) *The pointed space (E, 0) is three dimensional for every point 0.*

Proof. 1. To demonstrate the equivalence of α and β, it is sufficient to consider the planes P, Q passing through 0, the origin of (E, 0).

Let $(P \cup Q)$ denote the subspace of (E, 0) spanned by P, Q and let $d(X)$ denote the dimension of any subspace X of (E, 0). We know that

(1) $$d(P \cup Q) + d(P \cap Q) = d(P) + d(Q) = 2 + 2 = 4$$

and we shall show that if α is satisfied then $d(E) \leqslant 3$.

Now, if this is false, there exist four linearly independent vectors p_1, p_2, q_1, q_2 in (E, 0). Letting P be the plane spanned by p_1, p_2 and Q be that spanned by q_1, q_2, we then find that $d(P \cup Q) = 4$. On the other hand, however, (1) then gives $d(P \cap Q) = 0$, contrary to assumption. Hence $d(E) \leqslant 3$ and as E contains at least two distinct planes, we must have $d(E) = 3$.

Conversely, if β is satisfied, then $d(P \cup Q) \leqslant 3$ gives $d(P \cap Q) \geqslant 1$. This shows that either P and Q are the same or they intersect along a line.

2. Statement β implies Axiom V. For if E is of dimension 3, every plane P is the set of solutions of an equation $f(x) = a$, where f is a linear form, and a is a scalar. The half-spaces E_1, E_2 associated with P are the sets defined by $f(x) < a$ and $f(x) > a$ respectively.

3. Finally let us prove that Axiom V implies α or β. The notation adopted is that given in Axiom V.

(a) Proof for algebraists

We can assume that P passes through 0. Now let S be a complementary subspace of P, and let $A_i = S \cap E_i$ ($i = 1, 2$).

It is clear that E_1 and E_2 are the unions of planes parallel to P, and so A_1 and A_2 are the projections of E_1 and E_2 on S parallel to P. On the other hand, A_1 and A_2 are a partition of $S - \{0\}$ and $(x_1 \in A_1, x_2 \in A_2) \Rightarrow (0 \in [x_1, x_2])$. It quickly follows that S is a line, proving that $d(E) = 3$.

(b) Elementary proof using only Axioms I, II

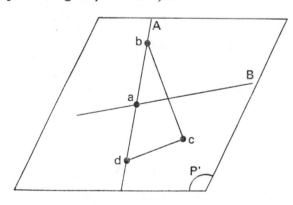

(b_1) Let P be an arbitrary plane, and (E_1, E_2) be the partition of $(E - P)$ associated with P. We show that every line A cutting P meets E_1 and E_2.

Put $a = A \cap P$, and let b be a point of A distinct from a. Suppose $b \in E_1$ and let c be an arbitrary point of E_2. If $c \in A$, there is nothing to prove. If not, the plane P' containing A and c meets P in $[b, c] \cap P$, a point distinct from a, and this means that the two planes meet in a line B.

Let d be a point of A in P' which is situated on the same side of B as c. As $[c, d]$ does not meet B, it does not meet P, and so $d \in E_2$.

(b_2) Now let P, Q be two distinct planes such that $a \in P \cap Q$.

Let A_1, A_2 be two distinct lines of Q passing through a. If one of them is in P, we are through. If not, A_1 contains a point $x_1 \in E_1$ and A_2 contains a point $x_2 \in E_2$. The interval $[x_1, x_2]$ meets P in a point a' distinct from a, and the line $\Delta(a, a')$ is then the required line.

Corollary 94.2. If Axiom V is satisfied, then the parallelism condition $(P \parallel P')$ *is equivalent to* $(P = P'$ *or* $P \cap P' = \varnothing)$.

Metric structure of space

We now investigate the consequences of Axioms I, II, III, IV. Just as in the affine study of E, we shall make extensive use of the metric structure of the planes of E. In fact, we shall rediscover the well-known result that most of the properties of a real inner product space are deducible from the metric properties of its 2-dimensional affine subspaces.

95. TRANSLATIONS AND PERPENDICULARITY

Proposition 95.1. Any translation of E is an isometry

Proof. If the map f is a translation and x, y points of E, then x, y, $f(x)$, $f(y)$ are all coplanar. We already know that any translation in a plane is an isometry.

Corollary 95.2. Any translation of E preserves the perpendicularity of two intersecting lines.

The proof is as in Corollary 44.4.

This corollary allows us to introduce the new concept:

Definition 95.3. Two lines A, B (intersecting or not) are said to be perpendicular if the lines parallel to them through the same point a are perpendicular.

By the above corollary, this definition is independent of a.

96. INNER PRODUCT

Definition 96.1. (inner product).

In the pointed space (E, 0), *an inner product is defined by the mapping* $(x, y) \rightarrow x \cdot y$ *from* $E \times E$ *into* R *satisfying:*

1. If 0, x, y *are not collinear,* $x \cdot y$ *is the inner product of the vectors* x, y *of the pointed plane* (P, 0) *containing* 0, x, y.

2. *If* 0, x, y *are collinear and not all coincident with* 0, $x \cdot y$ *is the inner product of the vectors* x, y *of the pointed line* (D, 0) *containing* 0, x, y.

3. *If* $x = y = 0$, $x \cdot y = 0$.

Proposition 96.2. In any pointed space (E, 0), *the map* $(x, y) \to x \cdot y$ *is symmetric, bilinear and positive in the sense that* $x \cdot x > 0$ *for every* $x \neq 0$. *Furthermore, for every* x, y, $d^2(x, y) = (x - y)^2$.

Proof. The relations $x \cdot y = y \cdot x$; $(\lambda x) \cdot y = \lambda(x \cdot y)$ and $x \cdot x > 0$ for $x \neq 0$ are all obvious. So is the relation $d^2(0, x) = x^2$. Hence, by Prop. 95.1,

$$d^2(x, y) = (x - y)^2 \quad \text{for all } x, y$$

It remains to show that, for all x, y, z,

(1) $$x \cdot (y + z) = x \cdot y + x \cdot z$$

Now this relation is valid in any pointed plane (P, 0), and so for all x, y, z such that 0, x, y, z are coplanar. In particular,

$$(b + c)^2 = b(b + c) + c(b + c) = b^2 + 2b \cdot c + c^2 \quad \text{for all } b, c$$

To prove (1) in the general case, let

$$m = \tfrac{1}{2}(y + z) = \text{mid-point of } (y, z)$$

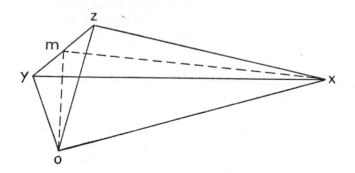

As $(0, y, z)$ and (x, y, z) are planar triples,

$$y^2 + z^2 = 2m^2 + 2(m - y)^2$$
$$(y - x)^2 + (z - x)^2 = 2(m - x)^2 + 2(m - y)^2$$

Subtracting term by term, we find

$$2x \cdot y + 2x \cdot z = 4x \cdot m = 2x(y + z)$$

which proves the result.

Thus $x \cdot y$ has all the properties of an inner product and the results of Chapter III apply.

To summarize, we can say that the following theorem is deducible from Axioms I, II, III, IV:

Theorem 96.3. For every point 0, there is a unique method of defining a real inner product space structure on E such that the zero vector is 0, the affine varieties of dimensions 1 and 2 are the lines and planes of E, and the distance obtained from the inner product coincides with the distance given for E.

97. APPLICATIONS TO TWO CLASSICAL THEOREMS

Most of the geometrical properties of space currently taught have simple proofs once we can use the algebraic tools that we have brought out. Here are two examples.

1. Let us say that a line D is perpendicular to a plane P (written $D \perp P$) if D is perpendicular to every line in P.

Proposition 97.1. Let A, B be two non-parallel lines in a plane P, and let D be a line. Then

$$(D \perp A \text{ and } D \perp B) \Rightarrow (D \perp P)$$

Proof. By applying a translation, we can reduce to the case where P, A, B, D all pass through 0. Suppose then that

$$a \in A, \qquad b \in B, \qquad d \in D \qquad \text{with} \quad a, b, d \neq 0$$

Every $x \in P$ can be written as $x = \lambda a + \mu b$ and in (E, 0), by hypothesis,

$$d \cdot a = 0 \quad \text{and} \quad d \cdot b = 0$$

Thus

$$d \cdot x = d \cdot (\lambda a + \mu b) = \lambda(d \cdot a) + \mu(d \cdot b) = 0$$

Hence $D \perp P$.

2. A classical theorem is the "theorem of the three perpendiculars". A little algebra reduces the proof to an obvious relation:

We assume that we know what is meant by the projection of a point x onto a plane or a line (foot of the perpendicular from x to the line or plane). It corresponds to the minimum distance.

Proposition 97.2. Let P be a plane contained in E, D a line in P and $a \in E$. Let p be the projection of a on P. Then the projections of p and a on D are the same.

Proof. $d^2(x, a) = d^2(a, p) + d^2(p, x)$ for $x \in D$.

Hence $d(a, x)$ is a minimum when $d(p, x)$ is a minimum and this proves the result.

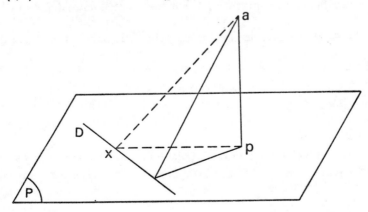

From this simplified version, it is easy to generalize to the case where E is any finite dimensional space, P any affine subspace of E and D any affine subspace of P. More generally, D can be replaced by any closed subset of P.

98. FURTHER TOPICS

We end our study of space by indicating a few topics which, thanks to the algebraic methods now at our disposal are easily adapted for classwork.

1. *Affine structure*

Study of affine transformations of E (particularly the dilation group), oblique projections, linear forms.
Study of convex sets.
Cones and cylinders (in relation to the group of homothetic transformations centre 0 and the translation group).

2. *Metric structure*

Orthogonal projection (diminishes distances).
Symmetries about a plane, line, point.
Isometries, rotations about an axis, sets stable under groups of isometries or similitudes such as cones, cylinders and spheres.

Exercises on Chapter IX

1. Let (D_i) be any family of lines such that any two lines intersect.
    Show that either all the lines pass through a common point, or all the lines are coplanar.

2. What happens in these circumstances when one knows only that any two of these lines are coplanar?

3. Let P, P′ be two distinct planes, and let (a_i) $(i = 1, 2, 3)$ (resp. (a_i')) be a triplet of distinct points of P (resp. P′).
    Show that if each $\Delta(a_i, a_j)$ (where $i \neq j$) meets $\Delta(a_i', a_j')$, the lines $\Delta(a_i, a_i')$, supposed defined, are parallel or concurrent, and that the three points $\Delta(a_i, a_j) \cap \Delta(a_i', a_j')$ are collinear.

4. Let A_1, A_2, A_3 be three planes, and a_1, a_2, a_3 be three points of the three-dimensional space E.
    Describe the set of homothetic transformations f such that

$$f(a_i) \in A_i \quad (i = 1, 2, 3)$$

5. Let D be a line in a vector space D, let X be a subset of D and let k be a number $\neq 0$.
    Find the set of points consisting of the centres of the homothetic transformations f of ratio k such that $f(D)$ meets X.

    Do the same replacing the line D by a plane P, then by an arbitrary subset Y of E.

6. Extend Exercises 3 and 4 of Chapter IV to space, first by direct transposition, then by replacing lines by planes.

7. Let E be a three-dimensional space, D a line in E and $0 \in E$.

Determine the subsets of E which are simultaneously stabilized by the rotations about D and the positive homothetic transformations centred at 0, distinguishing between the cases where $0 \in D$ and $0 \notin D$.

Repeat replacing the homothetic transformations by the translations parallel to a direction δ.

8. Let D be a line in space. A helicoidal displacement with axis D is defined to be any product f of translations parallel to D with an even number of symmetries about planes through D.

Show that the helicoidal displacements form a group isomorphic to $T \times R$.

9. Let f, g be two helicoidal displacements with axes A, B. Show that $f \circ g$ and $g \circ f$ are helicoidal displacements whose axes are symmetric about the line perpendicular to both A and B.

10. Define the arithmetical measure (in radians) of a pair (A, B) of half-lines in E with the same origin as the arithmetical measure $p(A, B)$ of $\widehat{AB}$, evaluated in a plane containing A and B (if this plane is not unique, the measure is obviously 0 or π).

Show that if (A, B) and (A', B') are any two pairs, the relation $p(A, B) = p(A', B')$ is equivalent to the existence of an isometry of E taking (A, B) into (A', B'). Show also that when equality holds there is always an even isometry and an odd isometry having this property.

A metrically based axiomatization

The axiomatization developed in the preceding chapters is based on vectors and the metric only appears after the vector structure has been thoroughly established.

Some teachers, however, are of the opinion that metric ideas are much more intuitive than vectorial ideas and are grasped more readily by the younger pupils. Considering that no systematic teaching of such pupils by vector methods has been tried before now, this is a point that can only be settled after a long period of experimentation with the different methods.

Even so, in case it emerges that it is better to start from metric concepts, I would like to add the following variation[8] of the original axiomatization, based on the mathematical formalization of the simple, everyday experience of folding a piece of paper about a line.

99 First axioms

Again the axioms fall into four groups.

Axioms I' and II' are the same as Axioms I and II in Chapter I.

Axiom III' consists of Axiom III_a of Chapter 2 with the triangular inequality added. Although it appears to involve a fixed field R, much of the work carries over for any totally ordered additive subgroup of R.

Axiom III'. There exists a map d from $\Pi \times \Pi$ into R_+, called distance, *such that:*

1. $d(y, x) = d(x, y)$ *for every* $x, y \in \Pi$.

2. *If D is an orientated line, $x \in D$, and l is a non-negative number, then there is a unique point $y \in D$ satisfying the relations $x \leqslant y$ and $d(x, y) = l$.*

3. $(x \in [a, b]) \Rightarrow (d(a, x) + d(x, b) = d(a, b))$.

---

8 The axiomatization given here is a modified version of that published previously in *Sur l'enseignement de la géométrie élémentaire* by the author in *Enseignement des Mathématiques*, pp. 75–129, Delachaux and Niestlé, Neufchâtel and Paris.
A simplification has been made by introducing Axiom I_b about parallels, and by turning the triangular inequality into a stricter inequality. This new axiomatization has the added advantage of avoiding the cumbersome method of defining lines as sets isometric to a given line.

4. *If $\{a, x, b\}$ are three non-collinear points,*

$$d(a, b) < d(a, x) + d(x, b) \quad \text{(strict triangular inequality)}$$

Elementary consequences of Axioms I', II', III'

1. Obviously, we have all consequences of III_a that we obtained previously. These are essentially summarized by Prop. 9.1 where it is shown that an orientated pointed line can be identified with the one-dimensional euclidean space R.

2. If a, x, b are any three points of Π,

$$d(a, b) \leqslant d(a, x) + d(x, b)$$

with equality holding if and only if $x \in [a, b]$.

3. Let X be a subset of Π, and let f be a mapping from X into Π.
   We say that f is an isometry if

$$(a, b \in X) \Rightarrow (d(a, b) = d(f(a), f(b)))$$

Property (2) above shows that any isometry preserves collinearity and the relation of "betweenness".

It follows that f maps intervals into intervals, lines into lines, parallel lines into parallel lines, and half-planes into half-planes. Any isometry of Π into itself is necessarily *onto* Π, and it is an isomorphism of the additive structure defined by Axioms I', II', III'.

Exercise. Let A_1, A_2 be two bounded plane convex polygons such that $A_1 \subset A_2$. Show that if their respective perimeters are l_1 and l_2, then $l_1 \leqslant l_2$ with strict equality holding only if $A_1 = A_2$.

This property provides us with an easy method of defining the boundary lengths of arbitrary bounded convex subsets.

100. FOLDING AXIOM (OR SYMMETRY AXIOM)

Before we can state this axiom, we need some terminology. Let $\Pi_1(D)$ and $\Pi_2(D)$ denote the two open half-planes defined by a line D, and call any isometry φ from $D \cup \Pi_1(D)$ onto $D \cup \Pi_2(D)$ which leaves the line D pointwise fixed a *folding map*, or *fold* about D.

Axiom IV'. For every line D, there exists at least one folding map about D.

There is no need to postulate the uniqueness of this map because it can be deduced so easily.

101. SYMMETRY ABOUT A LINE

Lemma 101.1. If D is a line, there is a unique fold about D.

Proof. Let $\Pi_1(D)$ and $\Pi_2(D)$ be the open half-planes defined by D. Let φ be a fold

about D and let $a \in \Pi_1(D)$. Put $a' = \varphi(a)$. Now the interval $[a, a']$ meets D in a point p, and no other point of D meets $[a, a']$. Hence,

$$d(a, a') < d(a, x) + d(x, a') = 2d(a, x) \quad \text{for all } x \in D \text{ with } x \neq p$$

As $d(a, a') = 2d(a, p)$, it follows that $d(a, p) < d(a, x)$, and the point p has the characteristic property, independent of φ, of being the nearest point on D to a. We say that p is the *orthogonal projection* or, more briefly, the *projection* of a onto D.

Now this projection is the mid-point of (a, a'), and so the point a' is simply that point which is symmetrically placed to a about p on the line joining a and p. Thus the image of a under an arbitrary folding map φ is unique, i.e. φ is unique.

Next, let $\hat{\varphi}$ denote the extension of φ to Π defined as follows:

$$\hat{\varphi}(x) = \varphi(x) \quad \text{for } x \in D \cup \Pi_1(D)$$
$$\hat{\varphi}(x) = \varphi^{-1}(x) \quad \text{for } x \in \Pi_2(D)$$

Lemma 101.2. *The extension $\hat{\varphi}$ is an isometry from Π onto itself. It is called the symmetry about D.*

Proof. In the first place, it is clear that φ is a mapping from Π onto itself. Now take $a, b \in \Pi$.

If $a, b \in D \cup \Pi_1(D)$, then trivially $d(\hat{\varphi}(a), \hat{\varphi}(b)) = d(a, b)$, because $\hat{\varphi}$ agrees with φ on $D \cup \Pi_1(D)$.

A similar argument holds if $a, b \in \Pi_2(D)$.

We suppose therefore that $a \in \Pi_1(D)$ and $b \in \Pi_2(D)$. We let $x = D \cap [a, b]$, and set

$$a' = \hat{\varphi}(a), b' = \hat{\varphi}(b)$$

In this case,

$$d(x, a) = d(x, a') \quad \text{and} \quad d(x, b) = d(x, b')$$

Hence

$$d(a', b') \leqslant d(a', x) + d(x, b') = d(a, x) + d(x, b) = d(a, b)$$

showing that $d(a', b') \leqslant d(a, b)$.

However, a precisely similar argument shows that $d(a, b) \leqslant d(a', b')$. Thus $d(a', b') = d(a, b)$, and the result is proved.

102. PERPENDICULARS AND PROJECTIONS

Definition 102.1. A line D' is said to be perpendicular to a line D (written $D' \perp D$) if $D' \neq D$ and D' coincides with its image under the symmetry about D.

Lemma 102.4. will show that this is a symmetric relation. Clearly, through any point $x \in D$, there is one and only one line per perpendicular to D, namely the line joining x to its symmetric image about D.

Lemma 102:2. 1. Two perpendicular lines D, D' always intersect.

2. *If* D, D' *are a pair of lines intersecting at* p, *then:*

$(D' \perp D) \Leftrightarrow$ (*Every point of* D' *projects onto the point* p *on* D)
$\Leftrightarrow$ (*There is a point of* D' *other than* p *which projects onto* p *on* D)

Proof. 1. The line D' contains at least one pair of distinct points x_1, x_2 symmetrically placed about D. Thus $[x_1, x_2]$ meets D.

2. Suppose $D' \perp D$ and $x \in D'$. The point x' which is symmetrically placed to x about D lies in D' and so the projection of x on D, being the point $D \cap [x, x']$, is indeed p.

Conversely, suppose D and D' intersect at p. Let x be any point of D' other than p whose projection on D is p, and take x' as the point which is symmetrically placed to x about D. As $[x, x']$ must meet D at p, it follows then that D', being the line joining the distinct points x, p, also contains x', and is therefore perpendicular to D.

Corollary 102.3. *If D, D' are a pair of perpendicular lines and f is an isometry of $D' \cup D$, then $f(D')$ is perpendicular to $f(D)$.*

This is evident because, by the above lemma, perpendicularity can be expressed by means of distances.

Lemma 102.4. *If $D' \perp D$, then $D \perp D'$.*

Proof. Suppose $D' \perp D$, and let p be their point of intersection.

If $x \in D$, then for every point x' of D' other than p,

$$d(x, x') = d(x, x'') \quad \text{where } x'' \text{ is that point symmetric to } x' \text{ about } D$$

Hence x' cannot be the projection of x on D' (uniqueness of the minimum) and this projection must then be p. The fact that D is perpendicular to D' now follows by Lemma 102.2.

Lemma 102.5. *If $D \perp D'$, then D is perpendicular to D'' if and only if $D' \parallel D''$.*

Proof. 1. Suppose $D \perp D'$ and $D' \parallel D''$.

The lines D, D'' meet at some point p, for otherwise $D'' \parallel D$, implying that $D' \parallel D$, which is not so. Also, the images under the symmetry about D of the parallel lines D' and D'' are parallel lines D', D_1'' (consequence 3 of Axiom III'). Thus D'' and D_1'' are parallel and pass through p. This shows that $D'' = D_1''$, i.e. $D \perp D''$.

2. Suppose $D \perp D'$ and $D \perp D''$.

Take x as any point on D'' not on D. By what we have just shown, the parallel to D' through x is perpendicular to D. It must coincide with D'' because the perpendicular to D from a point not on D is unique. In other words $D' \parallel D''$.

102.6. Applications.

If δ_1, δ_2 are a pair of directions, we say that they are perpendicular if there exists a pair of perpendicular lines with δ_1, δ_2 as directions. Lemmas 102.4 and 102.5 show that:

1. Perpendicularity is a symmetric, antireflexive (i.e. $\delta \perp \delta$ impossible) relation, and to every direction there is one and only one perpendicular direction.

2. Two lines are perpendicular if and only if their corresponding directions are perpendicular.

Remark. It follows from this that the mapping associating with each point $x \in \Pi$ its orthogonal projection on a line D is the same as that oblique projection on D with direction perpendicular to D.

Definition 102.7. Let a, b be two distinct points whose mid-point is 0. The perpendicular bisector *of (a, b) is defined to be the line through 0 perpendicular to* $\Delta(a, b)$.

Lemma 102.8. Let a, b be a pair of distinct points, and D *be their perpendicular bisector. Let* Π_a, Π_b *be the open-half planes defined by* D *containing a and b respectively. Then:*

$$(x \in D) \Rightarrow (d(x, a) = d(x, b));$$
$$(x \in \Pi_a) \Rightarrow (d(x, a) < d(x, b)); \qquad (x \in \Pi_b) \Rightarrow (d(x, b) < d(x, a))$$

Proof. Because *a* and *b* are symmetric about D,

$$(x \in D) \Rightarrow (d(x, a) = d(x, b))$$

If $x \in \Pi_a$, let $y = D \cap [x, b]$. Now, because $y \notin [a, x]$ (convexity of Π_a), we have

$$d(x, a) < d(x, y) + d(y, a) = d(x, y) + d(y, b) = d(x, b)$$

A similar argument holds for Π_b.

Corollary 102.9. $(x \in D) \Leftrightarrow (d(x, a) = d(x, b))$.

Corollary 102.10. (Comparison of transversals.)
    If p is the projection of x on the line containing a and b, then the relative ordering of $d(p, a)$ and $d(p, b)$ is the same as that of $d(x, a)$ and $d(x, b)$.

Proof. For $x \in D$, Π_a, or Π_b depending on whether $d(p, a) - d(p, b)$ is zero, strictly negative or strictly positive.
    This result can also be put in the form:
    The length of a transversal segment is a strictly monotonic increasing function of the length of its projection.
    Pythagorean theorem is really just an exact quantification of this result.

Corollary 102.11. If $(0, a, b)$ is a triangle with $d(0, a) = d(0, b)$ and $a \neq b$, then the projection of 0 onto the line joining a, b is the mid-point of (a, b).
    This is an immediate, but vitally important, consequence of Corollary 102.10.
    It can also be re-stated as follows:
    In any isosceles triangle, the line perpendicular to the base through the opposite vertex is an axis of symmetry for the triangle.

103. SYMMETRY ABOUT A POINT AND PRODUCTS OF SYMMETRIES

Definition 103.1. The symmetry about a point 0 is the mapping f from Π onto itself defined as follows:

$$f(0) = 0 \quad and, \ for \ x \neq 0, \quad f(x) = x'$$

where x' is the point on $\Delta(0, x)$ such that (x, x') has mid-point 0.
    Clearly $f^2 =$ identity, and $f(D) = D$, for every line D containing 0.

Theorem 103.2. The symmetry about 0 is equal to the product of any two symmetries whose axes pass through 0 and are mutually perpendicular.

Proof. Let D_1, D_2 be any pair of perpendicular lines through 0. Take $x \notin (D_1 \cup D_2)$. Let Δ_1, Δ_2 be the parallels to D_1 and D_2 through x, and let Δ_i' be the image of Δ_i under the

symmetry about $D_i (i = 1, 2)$. Then Δ'_i is clearly parallel to Δ_i $(i = 1, 2)$.

The rectangle formed by the two pairs of parallels Δ_1, Δ'_1 and Δ_2, Δ'_2 is symmetric about both lines D_1, D_2. Consequently the same is true for its diagonals, which means that these intersect at a point which is on both D_1 and D_2. This, of course, is 0. It now follows that the point symmetric to x about 0 is simply the opposite vertex, and we can pass from x to this point by taking the product of the symmetry about D_1 and that about D_2.

If $x \in D_1 \cup D_2$, this result holds for obvious reasons. Hence, in all cases, the result is proved.

Corollary 103.3. Symmetry about a point is always an isometry. It transforms any line onto a parallel line.
(Consider first the case where D passes through 0, then the general case.)

Application 103.4.

We shall call any quadrilateral (a, b, a', b'), in which the pairs (a, a'), (b, b') have the same mid-point, a parallelogram.

By the previous corollary, a non-collinear quadrilateral (a, b, a', b') is a parallelogram if and only if its vertices are all mutually distinct with

$$\Delta(a, b) \parallel \Delta(a', b') \quad \text{and} \quad \Delta(a, b') \parallel \Delta(a', b)$$

Since any parallelogram must have a centre of symmetry at the intersection of its diagonals, opposite sides are equal.

Lemma 103.5. Let D, D', A be three parallel lines.

1. *If D' is the line symmetric to D about A, every transversal meets the lines in three points x, x', a such that a is the mid-point (x, x').*

2. *Conversely, if there is a transversal D' with this property, D' is the line symmetric to D about A.*

Proof. 1. Suppose D and D' are symmetric about A. Let x, x', a be their points of intersection with some transversal. Let B be the perpendicular to A through a. The product of the symmetries about A and B, transform D to D'. Thus, by Theorem 103.2, these lines are symmetric about a and this means that a is the mid-point of (x, x'), as required.

2. If a is the mid-point of (x, x'), then D' is symmetric to D with respect to a. But D is also self-symmetric with respect to B. Hence, by Theorem 103.2 and its corollary, the line symmetric to D about A is the same as the line symmetric to D about a. Thus, D' is symmetric to D about A.

Theorem 103.6. (Weak form of Thales theorem.)
If three parallels D, D', A are cut by a transversal in three points x, x', a such that a is the mid-point of (x, x'), then the same is true for every transversal (i.e. D and D' are symmetric about every point of A).

This is an immediate consequence of Lemma 103.5.

Corollary 103.7. If n is any integer with $n \geqslant 2$, any given interval can be divided (uniquely) into n consecutive equal sub-intervals.

(Classical construction using a set of parallel lines passing through a set of points equally spaced on some auxiliary line.)

Obviously this corollary is only of interest when we suppose that we have only a few properties of R at our disposal, for instance, if we are assuming only that it is a totally ordered abelian group.

104. A POINTER TO SUBSEQUENT DEVELOPMENT

As Theorem 103.6 asserts the same property as that postulated by Axiom III_b, we have Axioms I, II, III at our disposal and the affine geometry of Π can be developed just as in Chapter II.

A perpendicularity was defined in 102.1 and Lemmas 102.2, 4, 5 show that this satisfies Axiom IV_a. Thus projection ratios of pairs of half-lines with the same origin can be defined and, as in no. 33, this ratio satisfies Axiom IV_b. The proof of this is quite simple:

If the half-lines A_1, A_2 originate at 0 and are collinear, this is obvious.

If they are not, taking $a_1 \in A_1$, $a_2 \in A_2$ with $d(0, a_1) = d(0, a_2) = 1$, we see that the perpendicular bisector D of (a_1, a_2) passes through 0, and symmetry about D interchanges A_1 and A_2. Thus $c(A_1, A_2) = c(A_2, A_1)$ because a symmetry is an isometry and it preserves perpendicularity.

Thus Axioms I, II, III, IV are all verified and we can proceed as before.

If a few metric ideas are to be developed before studying vector methods, it is quite possible to prove Pythagoras' theorem without using the inner product. Here is one such proof which uses no previous result about similarity of triangles nor angles of triangles:

Let D, D' be two half-lines with origin 0, let $x \in D$ and let k be the projection ratio of (D, D').

Let x' be the projection of x on the line containing D', let x'' be the projection of x' on the line containing D. Quite clearly, $\overline{0x''} = k^2 \overline{0x}$, showing that $x'' \in D$.

Suppose now (a, b, c) is any triangle, right-angled at a. Let p be the projection of a on $\Delta(b, c)$, α, β, γ the lengths of its sides, and k, k' be the projection ratios of the pairs of half-lines associated with b and c respectively in this triangle.

The previous result shows that $p \in [b, c]$, and so

$$\alpha = k^2\alpha + k'^2\alpha, \quad \text{or} \quad \alpha^2 = k^2\alpha^2 + k'^2\alpha^2, \quad \text{i.e.} \quad \alpha^2 = \beta^2 + \gamma^2$$

In particular, it follows from this that $|k|, |k'| \leqslant 1$.

Axiomatization of non-euclidean geometry

105. In my opinion, it is not really profitable to discuss with pupils the possible modifications that can be made to the given axiom system before they have thoroughly grasped this system and developed a certain mathematical maturity. Besides, euclidean geometry has such simplicity, and contains the seeds of so many basic ideas like group, vector space, inner product, that we inevitably lose something by studying it in conjunction with other geometries.

The complete opposite is true when the end of secondary education is reached or at the beginning of university education: at this point, the pupil has sufficient algebraic tools at his disposal to make a study of certain non-euclidean models extremely valuable, and it is very interesting to discover how few modifications to the axiomatization of the plane are needed to give the axioms of other geometries.

I will briefly indicate axioms for the "general" geometry of the plane, characterizing the planes that are euclidean or hyperbolic.

Again, the plane is a set Π, the lines subsets of Π, and the axioms fall into four groups.

(I″) *For every pair (x, y) of distinct points of Π, there is one and only one line containing x and y.*

(II″) *Every line can be totally ordered in two ways, and each ordering is the reverse of the other.*

(III″) *Axiom III of Appendix 1.*

(IV″) *(Folding axiom.) For every line D, there exists a partition of $(\Pi - D)$ into two non-empty sets Π_1, Π_2 such that*

1. $(x_1 \in \Pi_1, x_2 \in \Pi_2) \Rightarrow ([x_1, x_2] \cap D$ *is non-empty.)*

2. *There exists an isometry f from $\Pi_1 \cup D$ onto $\Pi_2 \cup D$ which fixes D pointwise.*

It is fairly easily[9] shown that the partitioning of Π into half-planes associated with a line is unique and, from this, comes the uniqueness of the corresponding folding map. We can go on to define symmetry about a line and show that it is an isometry of Π.

Through these symmetries, we obtain our perpendicularity, and the symmetries generate the isometry group of Π. As in the euclidean plane, the even isometries

---

9 The proofs of the first theorems are given in the author's article in *Enseignement des Mathématiques*, *loc. cit.*

(products of an even number of symmetries) form a group which is simply transitive on the set of closed half-lines.

If D is a line and x a point not on D, there is at least one parallel to D passing through x. If, for some pair (D_0, x_0), there is only one such parallel, we can show that the same is true of all pairs (D, x). When this happens, we say that the plane is euclidean, otherwise it is hyperbolic.

Axiomatization for the "little" geometry

"Little" geometry is the name we give to the geometry taught up to 14 years old. It does not use vectors explicitly, and segments are divided only in rational, not arbitrary, ratios. At this age, no attempt is made to teach geometry as a logical development: proofs of theorems are based on premises which are acceptable to the pupils because they appear intuitively true. In a sense, these premises are the axioms for little islands of logical deduction that we build.

Needless to say, it is vital that any definitions and language used in such teaching must be in sympathy with the scheme to be used systematically later on.

Also, it is desirable to have some guiding principle for choosing which fragments can be appropriately developed in a logical manner. My own opinion is that this is best done by giving an axiomatization in which the axioms are very strong and use only simple ideas such as congruence.

Axioms for the affine properties

The first two axioms are Axioms I and II, except that we restate Axiom II in terms of the relation of "betweenness" (see Halsted). Axiom IIIa is replaced by:

(III_a''') On the set of pairs $\Pi \times \Pi$, there is an equivalence relation $\sim$ satisfying the following properties:

1. $(x, y) \sim (y, x)$, for all x, y.

2. For every line D, and all $x, y, x' \in D$, there exists on either side of x' a unique point y such that $(x, y) \sim (x', y')$.

3. For every line D, and all $x, y, z, x', y', z' \in D$ such that $x \leqslant y \leqslant z$ and $x' \leqslant y' \leqslant z'$,

$$[(x, y) \sim (x', y') \quad \text{and} \quad (y, z) \sim (y', z')] \Rightarrow [(x, z) \sim (x', z')]$$

Axiom III_b stays the same.

The equivalence classes of the relation $\sim$ are called *distances*; they can be compared and added.

Theorem 12.3 may be deduced [10] from these axioms and it may even be shown that after choosing an origin, Π becomes a vector space over Q.

Thus, from these axioms, all the classical results about the affine structure of the plane can be derived.

Axioms for metric properties

Adjoin to the above axioms:

Either the triangular inequality III_4' and the folding Axiom IV', or Axiom IV_a and the following axiom, which is stronger than IV_b.

(IV_b''') *If* $(0, x, y)$ *is any non-collinear triplet, and* h *denotes the projection of* 0 *on the line* $\Delta(x, y)$, *then*

$$[d(h, x) = d(h, y)] \Leftrightarrow [d(0, x) = d(0, y)]$$

---

10 Not even Axiom II is required here. Suppose, more generally, that Axiom I is satisfied and each line Δ of Π, admits a torsion-free abelian group $G(\Delta)$ acting in a simply transitive manner. Then mid-points can be defined and, on postulating III_b, Theorem 12.3 can be proved. Also, it can be shown that the pointed planes $(\Pi, 0)$ are vector spaces over Q.

Alternative scheme for defining angles

Angles were defined in Chapter V in terms of the group of rotations about a point.

Here, I will give another method which stays closer to the idea of a pair of half-lines. Essentially, it entails the defining of an equivalence relation on the set of pairs of half-lines about an origin 0, thinking of angles as the corresponding equivalence classes, and defining an addition on the quotient set. The method closely follows that of defining vectors by starting with "localized" vectors; in fact, the two are so alike that both could be presented within a common framework. This is the procedure that I would like to adopt, leaving the reader to interpret the results both in terms of vectors and in terms of angles.

In the first case, the underlying set E is Π and $\mathscr{S}$ is the set of central symmetries of Π. In the second, E is a circle with centre 0 and $\mathscr{S}$ is the set of axial symmetries whose axes pass through 0.

The abstract scheme

Let E be a set with a collection $\mathscr{S}$ of permutations satisfying the following properties:

1. If $\sigma \in \mathscr{S}$, σ^2 is the identity.
2. If $x, y \in E$, there exists a unique $\sigma \in \mathscr{S}$ interchanging x and y.
3. If $\rho, \sigma, \rho', \sigma' \in \mathscr{S}$, and $\rho \cdot \sigma(x) = \rho' \cdot \sigma'(x)$ for some $x \in E$, then $\rho \cdot \sigma(x) = \rho' \cdot \sigma'(x)$ for all $x \in E$.

The products $\rho \cdot \sigma$, with $\rho, \sigma \in \mathscr{S}$, will be called *translations* of E.

Lemma α. Every product $\rho \cdot \sigma \cdot \tau$ of elements of $\mathscr{S}$ is an element of $\mathscr{S}$.

For let $a \in E$ and put $a' = \rho \cdot \sigma \cdot \tau(a)$. Let π be that element of $\mathscr{S}$ interchanging a and a'.

From $\rho \cdot \sigma \cdot \tau(a) = \pi(a)$, we get $\sigma \cdot \tau(a) = \rho \cdot \pi(a)$, and this implies that $\rho \cdot \sigma \cdot \tau = \pi$.

Corollary.[11] If $\rho, \sigma, \tau \in \mathscr{S}$ then $(\rho \cdot \sigma \cdot \tau)^2$ is the identity.

Now we introduce an equivalence relation on E × E.

We say that (a, b, c, d) is a *parallelogram* in E if that permutation interchanging

---

[11] Although apparently weaker, this is equivalent nevertheless to property 3 of translations.

a and c also interchanges b and d. We then define $(a, b) \sim (a', b')$ if (a, b, b', a') is a parallelogram.

Obviously,

$$[(a, b) \sim (a', b')] \Leftrightarrow [(a, a') \sim (b, b')]$$

It is clear that the relation $\sim$ is reflexive and symmetric. To show it is an equivalence relation, it remains to show only that it is transitive.

But if $(a, b) \sim (a', b')$ and $(a', b') \sim (a'', b'')$, there exists ρ in $\mathscr{S}$ such that $\rho(b) = a'$ and $\rho(a) = b'$, and σ in $\mathscr{S}$ such that $\sigma(a') = b''$ and $\sigma(b') = a''$.

Taking the permutation τ which interchanges a and b'', we find that $\sigma \cdot \rho \cdot \tau \cdot \sigma \cdot \rho(b) = a''$ and, by the above corollary, this shows that $\tau(b) = a''$ and $\tau(a'') = b$. Thus, $(a, b) \sim (a'', b'')$.

Lemma β. For all a, b, c, a', b', c',

$$[(a, b) \sim (a', b') \quad \text{and} \quad (b, c) \sim (b', c')] \Rightarrow [(a, c) \sim (a', c')]$$

Proof. The given relations are equivalent to the three relations

$$(a, a') \sim (b, b'), \qquad (b, b') \sim (c, c'), \qquad (a, a') \sim (c, c')$$

The proof is now obvious by transitivity.

Lemma γ. If $a, b, a' \in E$, there is a unique b' such that $(a, b) \sim (a', b')$.

Proof. The element b' is $\rho(a)$ where ρ is the element of $\mathscr{S}$ such that $a' = \rho(b)$.

We now have all that we need to define a group structure on $E \times E$. This has to be abelian because, in any parallelogram (a, b, b', a'),

$$(a, b) \sim (a', b') \quad \text{and} \quad (a, a') \sim (b, b')$$

We show that this group is isomorphic to the group of translations and that this coincides with the group of permutations of E which transform every pair (a, b) onto an equivalent pair.

Finally we show that whatever point ω of E we choose, we can always define an additive abelian group structure on E whose null element is ω. Its translation group is just the group previously defined.

The elements of $\mathscr{S}$ turn out to be the symmetries $x \to (a - x)$ of the group E. Conversely, it is clear that for every abelian group G, the symmetries $x \to (a - x)$ of G have the properties 1, 2, 3 required of $\mathscr{S}$, and the translation group associated with $\mathscr{S}$ is precisely the translation group of G.

List of symbols

(Each symbol is followed by the page number in which it first appears in the text)

Index of terms

(Each entry is followed by the indication of the section no.)

Bibliography

I have listed only a few works which may be of special interest to teachers.

I. *Works by Euclid or inspired by him*

EUCLID: French translation by Peyrard, Paris, Louis, 1840. Italian translation by Enriques, Bologna, Zanichelli, 1932. English translation by Heath, New York, Everyman's Library, 1956.

HILBERT: *Grundlagen der Geometrie*, Leipzig 1930.

HALSTED G. B.: *Géometrie rationnelle*, Paris, Gauthier-Villars, 1911.

II. *American works based on the concept of distance*

VEBLEN OSWALD, A system of axioms for geometry, *Trans. Amer. Math. Soc.*, vol. 5, 1904, pp. 343, 384.
The foundations of geometry, Ch. 1, *Monographs on topics of modern mathematics*, New York, 1955.

MOORE R. L., Sets of metrical hypotheses for geometry, *Trans. Amer. Math. Soc.*, vol. 9, 1908, pp. 487, 512.

FORDER H. G., *The foundations of Euclidean Geometry*, London 1927.

BIRKHOFF G. D., A set of postulates for plane geometry based on scale and protractor; *Ann. of Math.*, vol. 33, 1932.

BIRKHOFF G. D. and BEATLEY RALPH, *Basic Geometry*, New York 1941, and *Manual to Basic Geometry*.

GILLAM B. E., A new set of postulates for Euclidean geometry, *Revista de Ciencia*, vol. 42, 1940, pp. 869–899.

BLUMENTHAL L. M., *Theory and Application of Distance Geometry*, New York 1953.

MACLANE SAUNDERS, Metric postulates for plane geometry, *American Math. Monthly*, vol. 66, 1959.

Works of "School Mathematics Study Group" (Moise, Curtis, Dans, Walker). A manual at present being experimented with on a large scale, based on the ideas of Birkhoff.

III. *Recent works*

ARTIN E., *Geometric Algebra* (especially Chapter 4), Interscience Tracts in Pure and Applied Mathematics, New York, London 1957.

BACHMANN F., *Aufbau der Geometrie aus dem Spiegelungsbegriff*, Berlin, Springer, 1959.

BEHNKE H.; FLADT K.; Süss W., *Geometrie. Grundlagen der Mathematik*, Band II, Göttingen, Vandenhoeck and Rupecht, 1960.

BOULIGAND G., *Accès aux principes de la Géometrie Euclidienne*, Viubert 1951.

BRISAC R., *Exposé élémentaire des principes de la Géométrie Euclidienne*, Gauthier-Villars, 1955 (a work based on the group of displacements).

CHOQUET G., Sur l'enseignement de la géometrie élémentaire, from *L'Enseignement des Mathématiques*, Paris, Delachaux and Niestle.

REVUZ A., A detailed account of the above work (mimeographed).

CARTAN H., *Cours polycopié de Math.* 11. (Axiomatization for a part of plane geometry.)
KEREKJARTO B., *Les fondements de la géometrie*, t. 1, Budapest, Gauthier-Villars, 1955.
I.C.M.I. Seminar on Modern Teaching of Geometry, Mathematisk Institut, Aarhus Universitet, *Elementar Afdeling*, no. 7, 1960.

IV. *Textbooks of elementary geometry containing interesting ideas*

COSSART and THÉRON, *Mathématiques*, 4°, Bordas.
DELTHEIL and CAIRE, *Géométrie*, Paris, Baillière.
ENRIQUES E. and AMALDI U., *Elementi di Geometria ad uso delle scuola secondarie superiori*, Bologna, Zanichelli.
ROSATI C. and BENEDETTI P., *Geometria*, Rome, Dante Alighieri.
SEVERI F., *Geometria elementare*, Florence, Vallecchi.
CASTELNUOVO E., *Geometria intuitiva*, Florence, La nuova Italia.
KENNISTON E. and JULLY, *Plane Geometry*, Ginn and Co., London, 1946.
MORSE E., *Mathematics for High Schools: Geometry*, Yale University, New Haven, Connecticut, 1959.
PEREPELKIN D. I., *Cours de géométrie élémentaire*, Gostekhizdut, 1949.